Trigonometry FOR BEGINNERS

The Ultimate Step by Step Guide to Acing Trigonometry

By

Reza Nazari

All inquiries should be addressed to:
info@effortlessMath.com
www.EffortlessMath.com

ISBN: 978-1-63719-440-9

Published by: **Effortless Math Education Inc.**

for Online Math Practice Visit www.EffortlessMath.com

Welcome to
Trigonometry Prep

2024

Thank you for choosing Effortless Math for your Trigonometry preparation and congratulations on making the decision to take the Trigonometry course! It's a remarkable move you are taking, one that shouldn't be diminished in any capacity.

That's why you need to use every tool possible to ensure you succeed on the final exam with the highest possible score, and this extensive study guide is one such tool.

Trigonometry for Beginners is designed to be comprehensive and cover all the topics that are typically covered in a Trigonometry course. It provides clear explanations and examples of the concepts and includes practice problems and quizzes to test your understanding of the material. The textbook also provides step-by-step solutions to the problems, so you can check your work and understand how to solve similar problems on your own.

Additionally, this book is written in a user-friendly way, making it easy to follow and understand even if you have struggled with math in the past. It also includes a variety of visual aids such as diagrams, graphs, and charts to help you better understand the concepts.

Trigonometry for Beginners is flexible and can be used to supplement a traditional classroom setting, or as a standalone resource for self-study. With the help of this comprehensive textbook, you will have the necessary foundation to master the material and succeed in the Trigonometry course.

Effortless Math's Trigonometry Online Center

Effortless Math Online Trigonometry Center offers a complete study program, including the following:

- ✓ Step-by-step instructions on how to prepare for the Trigonometry test
- ✓ Numerous Trigonometry worksheets to help you measure your math skills
- ✓ Complete list of Trigonometry formulas
- ✓ Video lessons for all Trigonometry topics
- ✓ Full-length Trigonometry practice tests
- ✓ And much more…

No Registration Required

Visit **EffortlessMath.com/Trigonometry** to find your online Trigonometry resources.

How to Use This Book Effectively?

Look no further when you need a study guide to improve your math skills to succeed on the Trigonometry course. Each chapter of this comprehensive guide to the Trigonometry will provide you with the knowledge, tools, and understanding needed for every topic covered on the course.

It's very important that you understand each topic before moving onto another one, as that's the way to guarantee your success. Each chapter provides you with examples and a step-by-step guide of every concept to better understand the content that will be on the course. To get the best possible results from this book:

- **Begin studying long before your final exam date**. This provides you ample time to learn the different math concepts. The earlier you begin studying for the test, the sharper your skills will be. Do not procrastinate! Provide yourself with plenty of time to learn the concepts and feel comfortable that you understand them when your test date arrives.
- **Practice consistently**. Study Trigonometry concepts at least 30 to 40 minutes a day. Remember, slow and steady wins the race, which can be applied to preparing for the Trigonometry test. Instead of cramming to tackle everything at once, be patient and learn the math topics in short bursts.
- Whenever you get a math problem wrong, **mark it off, and review it later** to make sure you understand the concept.
- Start each session by **looking over the previous material.**
- Once you've reviewed the book's lessons, **take a practice test at the back of the book** to gauge your level of readiness. Then, review your results. Read detailed answers and solutions for each question you missed.
- **Take another practice test** to get an idea of how ready you are to take the actual exam. Taking the practice tests will give you the confidence you need on test day. Simulate the Trigonometry testing environment by sitting in a quiet room free from distraction. Make sure to clock yourself with a timer.

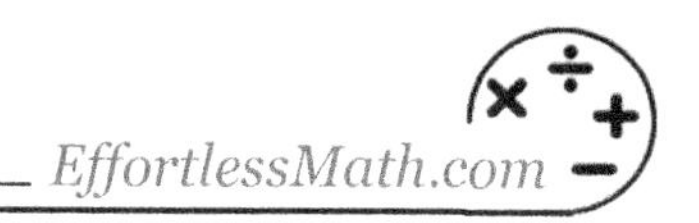

Looking for more?

Visit EffortlessMath.com/Trigonometry to find hundreds of Trigonometry worksheets, video tutorials, practice tests, Trigonometry formulas, and much more.

Or scan this QR code.

No Registration Required.

What is Trigonometry?

Trigonometry is a branch of mathematics that studies the relationships between the angles and sides of triangles, particularly right triangles. The word "trigonometry" comes from the Greek words "trigonon" (triangle) and "metron" (measure). Trigonometry is widely used in various fields, including physics, engineering, astronomy, navigation, and surveying.

In a right triangle, which has one angle measuring 90 degrees, trigonometry focuses on the ratios of the side lengths, using the angles as the primary means of comparison. The three primary trigonometric functions are:

- **Sine (sin)**: The ratio of the length of the side opposite an angle to the length of the hypotenuse (the longest side of the triangle, opposite the right angle).
- **Cosine (cos)**: The ratio of the length of the side adjacent to an angle to the length of the hypotenuse.
- **Tangent (tan)**: The ratio of the length of the side opposite an angle to the length of the side adjacent to that angle.

These functions have a range of applications, from solving triangles with unknown sides or angles to modeling periodic phenomena like sound waves and oscillations.

Trigonometry also involves the study of inverse trigonometric functions, which help to determine the angles when given the ratios of the sides, as well as various identities and formulas that simplify complex trigonometric expressions.

In addition to right triangles, trigonometry can be extended to include non-right triangles by using the Law of Sines and the Law of Cosines. These laws enable the calculation of unknown side lengths and angles in any triangle.

Overall, trigonometry is an essential mathematical tool with a wide range of applications across various scientific disciplines and real-world problems.

Importance and Applications of Trigonometry

Trigonometry is a vital branch of mathematics that focuses on the relationships between the angles and sides of triangles, particularly right-angled triangles. Its importance and applications span across numerous fields, making it an essential tool for understanding and solving a wide range of problems.

- **Engineering**: Trigonometry is indispensable in engineering disciplines such as civil, mechanical, and electrical. It helps engineers design and analyze structures, determine forces and stresses, and calculate the stability and efficiency of systems.

- **Physics**: In physics, trigonometry is used to analyze motion, forces, and waves. It helps physicists understand and predict the behavior of objects and phenomena like projectiles, pendulums, and light waves.

- **Astronomy**: Trigonometry plays a crucial role in understanding celestial bodies' positions and distances. Astronomers use it to calculate the size, distance, and movement of stars, planets, and other astronomical objects.

- **Navigation**: In navigation, trigonometry helps determine the position, distance, and direction of objects on Earth or in space. It is essential for pilots, sailors, and satellite operators to calculate routes, bearings, and other navigational information.

- **Architecture and Construction**: Architects and builders use trigonometry to design and construct buildings, bridges, and other structures. It helps them determine angles, heights, and lengths, ensuring the stability and aesthetic appeal of their creations.

- **Surveying and Mapping**: Trigonometry is crucial for surveyors and cartographers who need to measure distances, angles, and elevations to create accurate maps and land surveys.

- **Computer Graphics and Animation**: Trigonometry is used in computer graphics and animation to create realistic and accurate 3D models, calculate the perspective, and simulate movement and rotation.

- **Medicine**: In medical imaging, trigonometry assists in analyzing and interpreting data from X −rays, CT scans, and MRIs, which helps diagnose and treat various health conditions.

In summary, trigonometry is a vital mathematical tool with diverse applications in numerous fields. It helps us understand and solve complex problems related to angles, distances, and relationships between them, making it indispensable for modern science and technology.

Trigonometry in Real Life

Trigonometry, a branch of mathematics focused on the relationships between angles and sides of triangles, has numerous real-life applications. These practical uses showcase the relevance and importance of trigonometry in everyday life:

- Construction and Architecture: Trigonometry is used to design and build structures like buildings, bridges, and dams. It helps determine angles, heights, and lengths to ensure the stability and aesthetic appeal of structures.
- Navigation: Pilots, sailors, and GPS systems rely on trigonometry to calculate positions, distances, and directions of objects on Earth or in space. This information is vital for determining routes, bearings, and other navigational data.
- Surveying and Mapping: Trigonometry is essential for surveyors and cartographers to measure distances, angles, and elevations accurately, enabling them to create detailed maps and land surveys.
- Physics: In real-world physics problems, trigonometry is used to analyze motion, forces, and waves.
- Engineering: Engineers in various fields, including civil, mechanical, and electrical engineering, use trigonometry to design and analyze structures, calculate forces and stresses, and assess the stability and efficiency of systems.
- Astronomy: Trigonometry plays a crucial role in understanding celestial bodies' positions, distances, and movement. It helps astronomers calculate the size, distance, and movement of stars, planets, and other astronomical objects.
- Telecommunications: Trigonometry is used to determine the angles and distances necessary for signal transmission in cell phone towers, satellite dishes, and other communication systems.

- Computer Graphics and Animation: In the world of digital media, trigonometry is used to create realistic 3D models, calculate perspective, and simulate movement and rotation in computer graphics and animations.
- Medicine: Trigonometry helps analyze and interpret medical imaging data, such as X –rays, CT scans, and MRIs. This information assists in diagnosing and treating various health conditions.
- Music Theory: Trigonometry is used in analyzing sound waves, frequencies, and harmonics, which helps in understanding and creating music.

In summary, trigonometry has extensive real-life applications across various fields, making it an indispensable tool for understanding and solving practical problems related to angles, distances, and their relationships.

Contents

CHAPTER

1 Angles and Measurement

Math topics that you'll learn in this chapter:

- ☑ Degrees and Radians
- ☑ Angle Conversions
- ☑ Angle Addition and Subtraction Formulas
- ☑ Angles of Rotation
- ☑ Function Values from the Calculator
- ☑ Reference Angles and the Calculator
- ☑ Coterminal Angles and Reference Angles
- ☑ Arc Length and Sector Area

Degrees and Radians

- Degrees and radians are two systems for measuring angles. Both are used in various fields of mathematics, physics, and engineering. Understanding their differences and how to work with them is essential when dealing with trigonometry, geometry, and calculations involving angles.
  - **Degrees:** The degree system is based on dividing a circle into 360 equal parts, with each part representing one degree (1°). Degrees are a widely used unit of angle measurement, and they can be further divided into minutes (') and seconds (") for more precise measurements. There are 60 minutes in a degree and 60 seconds in a minute.
  - For example, an angle of 45° represents 45 parts out of the 360 parts of a circle, and an angle of 90° corresponds to a quarter of a circle.
  - **Radians:** The radian system is based on the radius of a circle. An angle of one radian is formed when the length of the arc between the two radii is equal to the length of the radius. In terms of a circle, there are 2π radians in a full circle, where π (pi) is the mathematical constant approximately equal to 3.14159.
  - For example, an angle of $\frac{\pi}{4}$ radians corresponds to $\frac{1}{8}$ of a circle, and an angle of $\frac{\pi}{2}$ radians corresponds to $\frac{1}{4}$ of a circle.

Example:

A wheel rotates at a constant speed of 5 revolutions per second. Express the angular velocity of the wheel in both degrees per second and radians per second.

Solution: One revolution is equal to 360 degrees or 2π radians.

Degrees per second: Since there are 360 degrees in one revolution, we can calculate the angular velocity in degrees per second by multiplying the number of revolutions (5) by 360:

$$\text{Degrees per second} = 5\frac{revolutions}{second} \times 360\frac{degrees}{revolution} = 1{,}800\frac{degrees}{second}$$

Radians per second: Similarly, we can calculate the angular velocity in radians per second by multiplying the number of revolutions (5) by 2π:

$$\text{Radians per second} = 5\frac{revolutions}{second} \times 2\pi\frac{radians}{revolution} \approx 31.4159\frac{radians}{second}$$

Angle Conversions

- To convert degrees to radians, use this formula: $Radian = Degrees \times \frac{\pi}{180}$.
- To convert radians to degrees, use this formula: $Degrees = Radian \times \frac{180}{\pi}$.

Examples:

Example 1. Convert 120 degrees to radians.

Solution: Use this formula: $Radian = Degrees \times \frac{\pi}{180}$.

Therefore: $Radian = 120 \times \frac{\pi}{180} = \frac{120\pi}{180} = \frac{2\pi}{3}$.

Example 2. Convert $\frac{\pi}{3}$ to degrees.

Solution: Use this formula: $Degrees = Radians \times \frac{180}{\pi}$.

Then: $Degrees = \frac{\pi}{3} \times \frac{180}{\pi} = \frac{180\pi}{3\pi} = 60$.

Example 3. Convert $\frac{2\pi}{5}$ to degrees.

Solution: Use this formula: $Degrees = Radians \times \frac{180}{\pi}$.

Therefore: $Degrees = \frac{2\pi}{5} \times \frac{180}{\pi} = \frac{360\pi}{5\pi} = 72$.

Example 4. Convert 45 degrees to radians.

Solution: Use this formula: $Radian = Degrees \times \frac{\pi}{180}$.

Therefore: $Radian = 45 \times \frac{\pi}{180} = \frac{45\pi}{180} = \frac{\pi}{4}$.

Example 5. Convert 420 degrees to radians.

Solution: Use this formula: $Radian = Degrees \times \frac{\pi}{180}$.

Therefore: $Radian = 420 \times \frac{\pi}{180} = \frac{420\pi}{180} = \frac{7\pi}{3}$.

Example 6. Convert $\frac{3\pi}{10}$ to degrees.

Solution: Use this formula: $Degrees = Radians \times \frac{180}{\pi}$.

Therefore: $Degrees = \frac{3\pi}{10} \times \frac{180}{\pi} = \frac{540\pi}{10\pi} = 54$.

Angle Addition and Subtraction Formulas

- Angle addition and subtraction are important concepts in trigonometry and geometry that deal with the operations of combining and separating angles.
  - **Degrees:** A full circle is divided into 360 degrees, which means one degree is $\frac{1}{360}th$ of a full rotation. To add or subtract angles in degrees, simply perform the arithmetic operation between the degree values.
    For example, if angle $A = 30°$ and angle $B = 45°$:
    Angle addition: $A + B = 30° + 45° = 75°$
    Angle subtraction: $A - B = 30° - 45° = -15°$ (a negative result indicates the angle is measured in the opposite direction)
  - **Radians:** A radian is another unit of angular measurement, and it is the SI unit for angles. One radian is defined as the angle subtended at the center of a circle by an arc whose length is equal to the radius of the circle. There are 2π radians in a full circle (approximately 6.283 radians).
  - To add or subtract angles in radians, perform the arithmetic operation between the radian values.
    For example, if angle $C = \frac{\pi}{6}$ radians and angle $D = \frac{\pi}{4}$ radians:
    Angle addition: $C + D = \frac{\pi}{6} + \frac{\pi}{4} = \frac{2\pi+3\pi}{12} = \frac{5\pi}{12}$ radians
    Angle subtraction: $C - D = \frac{\pi}{6} - \frac{\pi}{4} = \frac{(2\pi - 3\pi)}{12} = -\frac{\pi}{12}$ radians

Examples:

Example 1. If angle $A = 95°$ and angle $B = -33°$, calculate $A + B$ and $A - B$.

Solution: To add or subtract angles in degrees, simply perform the arithmetic operation between the degree values:

$A + B = 95° + (-33°) = 95° - 33° = 62°$

$A - B = 95° - (-33°) = 95° + 33° = 128°$

Example 2. If angle $A = \frac{3\pi}{8}$ and angle $B = \frac{2\pi}{7}$, calculate $A + B$ and $A - B$.

Solution: To add or subtract angles in degrees, simply perform the arithmetic operation between the radian values:

$A + B = \frac{3\pi}{8} + \frac{2\pi}{7} = \frac{21\pi+16\pi}{56} = \frac{37\pi}{56}$ radians

$A - B = \frac{3\pi}{8} - \frac{2\pi}{7} = \frac{21\pi-16\pi}{56} = \frac{5\pi}{56}$ radians

Angles of Rotation

- In trigonometry, an angle is defined by a ray that revolves around its endpoint. Each position of the rotated ray, relative to its starting position, creates an angle of rotation. The letter θ is used to name the angle of rotation.
- The initial position of the ray is called the initial side of the angle and the final position is called the terminal side of the angle.
- An angle is said to be in standard position when the initial side is along the positive x −axis and its endpoint is at the origin.
- Angles in a standard position that have the same terminal side are coterminal.
- The reference angle, θ_{ref}, is the smallest possible angle formed by the terminal side of the given angle with the x −axis.

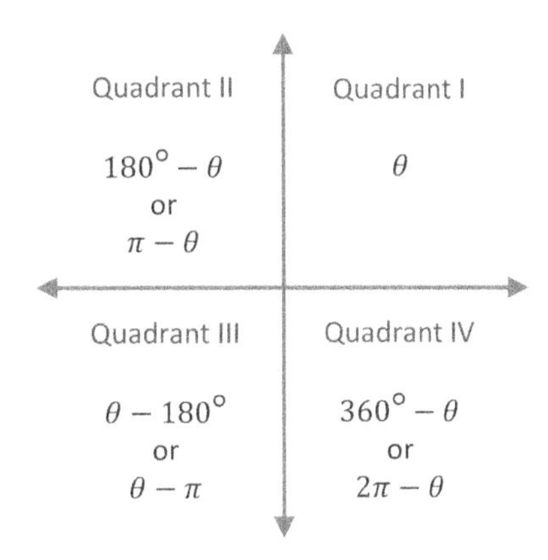

Examples:

Example 1. Find the coterminal of 30° in the interval $-360° < \theta < 360°$.

Solution: You can find coterminal angles by adding or subtracting multiples of integers of 360°.

$\theta = 30° + 360° = 390°$

$\theta = 30° - 360° = -330°$

The coterminal angle is −330°.

Example 2. Find the reference angle of 120°.

Solution: You know that 120° lies in quadrant II. $180° - 120° = 60°$

Function Values from the Calculator

- You can use a calculator to find the value of trigonometric functions.
- Press MODE in your calculator. The third line of that menu is DEGREE and RADIAN. These are two common measures of angles.
- These steps follow for evaluating trigonometric functions on a scientific calculator.
    - Select the correct mode (degrees or radians).
    - Click the *sin*, *cos*, or *tan* button.
    - Enter the angle measurement.
    - Click 'enter'.

Examples:

Example 1. Find $sin\,225°$ to four decimal places.

Solution:

$sin\,225° = -0.7071$

Example 2. Find $sec\,44°$ to four decimal places.

Solution:

$sec\,44° = 1.3901$

Example 3. Find $cot\,56°$.

Solution:

$cot\,56° = 0.67$

Example 4. Find $cos\,-130°$ to four decimal places.

Solution: $cos\,-130° = cos\,130° = -0.6427$.

Reference Angles and the Calculator

- If θ is the measure of an angle $90^{\circ} < \theta < 360^{\circ}$, the reference angle will be:

	Second Quadrant	Third Quadrant	Fourth Quadrant
Reference Angle	$180° - \theta$	$\theta - 180°$	$360° - \theta$
$sin\,\theta$	$sin(180° - \theta)$	$-sin(\theta - 180°)$	$-sin(360° - \theta)$
$cos\,\theta$	$-cos(180° - \theta)$	$-cos(\theta - 180°)$	$cos(360° - \theta)$
$tan\,\theta$	$-tan(180° - \theta)$	$tan(\theta - 180°)$	$-tan(360° - \theta)$

Example:

If $sin\,\theta = 0.7547$, find two positive values of θ that are less than $360°$.

Solution: Use the calculator to find $arc\,sin\,0.7547$.

$arc\,sin\,0.7547 = 49°$

The measure of the reference angle is $49°$. The sine is negative in the third and fourth quadrants.

In the third quadrant:

$49° = \theta - 180°$

$49° + 180° = \theta$

$\theta = 229°$

In the fourth quadrant:

$49° = 360° - \theta$

$360° - 49° = \theta$

$\theta = 311°$

Coterminal Angles and Reference Angles

- Coterminal angles are equal angles.
- To find a coterminal of an angle, add or subtract 360 degrees (Or 2π for radians) from the given angle.
- The reference angle is the smallest angle you can make from the terminal side of an angle with the x −axis.

Examples:

Example 1. Find a positive and a negative coterminal angle to angle 65°.

Solution: By definition, we have:

$65^\circ - 360^\circ = -295^\circ$,

$65^\circ + 360^\circ = 425^\circ$.

-295° and a 425° are coterminal with a 65°.

Example 2. Find a positive and a negative coterminal angle to angle $\frac{\pi}{2}$.

Solution: According to the definition, we have:

$\frac{\pi}{2} + 2\pi = \frac{5\pi}{2}$,

$\frac{\pi}{2} - 2\pi = -\frac{3\pi}{2}$.

This means that $\frac{5\pi}{2}$ and a $-\frac{3\pi}{2}$ are coterminal with a $\frac{\pi}{2}$.

Example 3. Find a positive and a negative coterminal angle to angle 25°.

Solution: According to the definition, we have:

$25^\circ - 360^\circ = -335^\circ$,

$25^\circ + 360^\circ = 385^\circ$.

-335° and a 385° are coterminal with a 25°.

Arc Length and Sector Area

- To find a sector of a circle, use this formula:
- Area of a sector $= \pi r^2 \left(\frac{\theta}{360}\right)$.
- Where r is the radius of the circle and θ is the central angle of the sector.
- To find the arc of a sector of a circle, use this formula:
- Arc of a sector $= \left(\frac{\theta}{180}\right) \pi r$.

Examples:

Example 1. Find the length of the arc. Round your answers to the nearest tenth. $(\pi = 3.14)$, $r = 24\ cm$, $\theta = 60°$

Solution: Use this formula: Length of a sector $= \left(\frac{\theta}{180}\right) \pi r$.

Therefore:

Length of a sector $= \left(\frac{60}{180}\right) \pi(24) = \left(\frac{1}{3}\right) \pi(24) = 8 \times 3.14 \cong 25.1\ cm$.

Example 2. Find the area of the sector. $r = 6\ ft$, $\theta = 90°$, $(\pi = 3.14)$

Solution: Use this formula: Area of a sector $= \pi r^2 \left(\frac{\theta}{360}\right)$.

Therefore:

Area of a sector $= (3.14)(6^2)\left(\frac{90}{360}\right) = (3.14)(36)\left(\frac{1}{4}\right) = 28.26\ ft^2$.

Example 3. If the length of the arc is 18,84 cm,where $r = 4\ cm$. Find the area of the sector. $(\pi = 3.14)$

Solution: Use this formula: Arc of a sector $= \left(\frac{\theta}{180}\right) \pi r$.

Then:

$18.84 = (3.14)(4)\left(\frac{\theta}{180}\right) \rightarrow 18.84 = 12.56\left(\frac{\theta}{180}\right) \rightarrow \theta = 270°$,

Now, use this formula: Area of a sector $= \pi r^2 \left(\frac{\theta}{360}\right)$.

Therefore: Area of a sector $= \left(\frac{270}{360}\right)(3.14)(4)^2 = 37.68\ cm^2$.

Chapter 1: Practices

Solve.

1) Alex is preparing for a cycling competition that takes place on a circular track. The track has a circumference of 100 meters. Alex wants to determine how many complete revolutions he needs to complete in order to cover a certain distance. Help Alex solve the following problem:

   Alex wants to cycle a distance of 400 meters. How many complete revolutions does he need to make around the track to cover this distance? Express your answer in both degrees and radians.

2) A bicycle tire rotates at a consistent speed of 10 revolutions per second. How would you express the angular velocity of this tire in both degrees per second and radians per second?

3) A ceiling fan spins at a constant rate of 2 revolutions per second. Can you determine the angular velocity of the fan in both degrees per second and radians per second?

Convert degrees to radians and radians to degrees.

4) $445°$
5) $130°$
6) $432°$
7) $1140°$
8) $1,000°$
9) 7π
10) $\frac{3\pi}{18}$
11) $\frac{10\pi}{9}$
12) $\frac{9\pi}{5}$
13) $\frac{15\pi}{6}$

Calculate.

14) $137° + 16° =$

15) $76° - 109° =$

16) $24° + (-55°) =$

17) $177° - 22° =$

18) $68° - 9° =$

19) $\frac{4\pi}{5} + \frac{7\pi}{15} =$

20) $\frac{6\pi}{9} - \frac{\pi}{27} =$

21) $\frac{2\pi}{8} + \frac{2\pi}{11} =$

22) $\frac{\pi}{2} - \frac{14\pi}{5} =$

23) $\frac{5\pi}{24} + \frac{13\pi}{8} =$

Find.

24) Find the reference angle of 130°. __________

25) Find the reference angle of 150°. __________

26) Find the reference angle of 115°. __________

27) Find the reference angle of 95°. __________

Find angles to four decimal places.

28) $csc\ 66°$

29) $sec\ 56°$

30) $cos\ 120°$

31) $tan\ 44°$

Solve.

32) Find two positive values of 55° that are less than 360°. __________

33) Find two positive values of 83° that are less than 360°. __________

Find a coterminal angle between 0° and 360° for each angle provided.

34) $-310° =$

36) $-440° =$

35) $-325° =$

37) $640° =$

Find a coterminal angle between 0 and 2π for each given angle.

38) $\frac{14\pi}{5} =$

41) $\frac{29\pi}{12} =$

39) $-\frac{16\pi}{9} =$

42) $-\frac{14\pi}{9}$

40) $\frac{41\pi}{18} =$

43) $\frac{22\pi}{7}$

Find the length of each arc. Round your answers to the nearest tenth.

44) $r = 14\ ft,\ \theta = 45°$

46) $r = 26\ m,\ \theta = 90°$

45) $r = 18\ m,\ \theta = 60°$

47) $r = 20\ m,\ \theta = 120°$

Find the area of the sector. Round your answers to the nearest tenth.

48) $r = 4\ m,\ \theta = 20°$

50) $r = 8\ m,\ \theta = 90°$

49) $r = 2\ m,\ \theta = 45°$

51) $r = 4\ m,\ \theta = 135°$

Chapter 1: Answers

1) 1,440 degrees, 8π radians
2) 3,600 $\frac{degrees}{second}$, $20\pi\ \frac{radians}{second}$
3) 720 $\frac{degrees}{second}$, $4\pi\ \frac{radians}{second}$
4) $\frac{89\pi}{36}$
5) $\frac{13\pi}{18}$
6) $\frac{12\pi}{5}$
7) $\frac{19\pi}{3}$
8) $\frac{50\pi}{9}$
9) 1260°
10) 30°
11) 200°
12) 324°
13) 450°
14) 153°
15) −33°
16) −31°
17) 155°
18) 59°
19) $\frac{19\pi}{15}$
20) $\frac{17\pi}{27}$
21) $\frac{19\pi}{44}$
22) $-\frac{23\pi}{10}$
23) $\frac{11\pi}{6}$
24) 50°
25) 30°
26) 65°
27) 85°
28) 1.0946
29) 1.7882
30) −0.5
31) 0.9656
32) $\theta = 235°$
$\theta = 305°$
33) $\theta = 263°$
$\theta = 277°$
34) 50°
35) 35°
36) 280°
37) 280°
38) $\frac{4\pi}{5}$
39) $\frac{2\pi}{9}$
40) $\frac{5\pi}{18}$
41) $\frac{5\pi}{12}$
42) $\frac{4\pi}{9}$
43) $\frac{8\pi}{7}$
44) 11.0
45) 18.8
46) 40.8
47) 41.9
48) 2.8
49) 1.6
50) 50.2
51) 18.8

CHAPTER

2 Right Triangle Trigonometry

Math topics that you'll learn in this chapter:

- ☑ Pythagorean Theorem
- ☑ Trigonometric Ratios
- ☑ Solving Right Triangles
- ☑ Special Right Triangles

Pythagorean Theorem

- The Pythagorean Theorem is a fundamental principle in geometry that states that in a right-angled triangle, the square of the length of the hypotenuse (the side opposite the right angle) is equal to the sum of the squares of the lengths of the other two sides. Mathematically, it can be expressed as:

$$a^2 + b^2 = c^2$$

- where $'a'$ and $'b'$ are the lengths of the two shorter sides (legs) and $'c'$ is the length of the hypotenuse. This theorem is named after the ancient Greek mathematician Pythagoras, who is credited with its discovery, although it was known and used by various civilizations before him.

Examples:

Example 1. A ladder is placed against a wall, with the base of the ladder 5 meters from the wall. If the ladder is 13 meters long, what is the height at which the ladder touches the wall?

Solution: The height at which the ladder touches the wall is approximately 12 meters. This can be found using the Pythagorean Theorem, where the ladder represents the hypotenuse, the distance from the base of the ladder to the wall is one leg, and the height at which the ladder touches the wall is the other leg of a right triangle. Specifically, we have $h^2 + 5^2 = 13^2$, which simplifies to $h^2 = 169 - 25 = 144$, and therefore $h = \sqrt{144} = 12$.

Example 2. A right triangle has a hypotenuse of length 10 cm and one leg of length 6 cm. What is the length of the other leg?

Solution: Using the Pythagorean Theorem, we can find the length of the other leg of the right triangle:

Let the length of the other leg be "x". Then, we have: $x^2 + 6^2 = 10^2$

Simplifying and solving for x, we get:

$$x^2 + 36 = 100 \rightarrow x^2 = 64 \rightarrow x = \sqrt{64} \rightarrow x = 8$$

Therefore, the length of the other leg of the right triangle is 8 cm.

Trigonometric Ratios

- Trigonometry is a branch of math that deals with the relationship between the angles and sides of a right-angled trigon. There are 6 trigonometric ratios: sine, cosine, tangent, secant, cosecant, and cotangent. These ratios are written as *sin*, *cos*, *tan*, *sec*, *cosec* or *csc*, and *cot* briefly. Trigonometric ratios could be used to determine the ratios of any 2 sides out of a complete 3 sides of a right-angled trigon in terms of the respective angles.

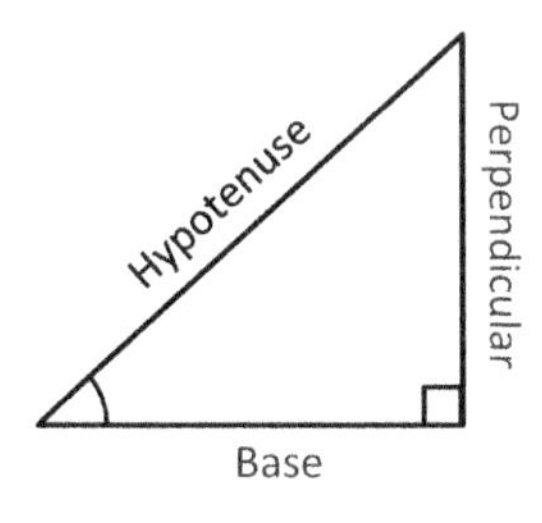

- The 6 trigonometric ratios will be outlined as:
  - **sine:** The ratio of the perpendicular side of the angle to the hypotenuse.
  - **cosine:** The ratio of the side adjacent to its angle to the hypotenuse.
  - **tangent:** The ratio of the opposite side of the angle to the adjacent side of its angle.
  - **cosecant:** Cosecant could be defined as a multiplicative inverse of sine.
  - **secant:** Secant could be defined as a multiplicative inverse of cosine.
  - **cotangent:** Cotangent could be defined as the multiplicative inverse of the tangent.

Examples:

Example 1. In a right-angled trigon, right-angled at B, the hypotenuse is 12 cm, the base 6 cm, and the perpendicular is 4 cm. If $\angle ACB = \theta$, then find the trigonometric ratio of $sin\,\theta$, and $cos\,\theta$.

Solution: We know that $sin\,\theta = \frac{perpendicular}{hypotenuse}$ and $cos\,\theta = \frac{base}{hypotenuse}$. So we put values of the hypotenuse, base, and perpendicular in these formulas to find the trigonometric ratio of $sin\,\theta$, and $cos\,\theta$: $sin\,\theta = \frac{perpendicular}{hypotenuse} \rightarrow sin\,\theta = \frac{4}{12} = \frac{1}{3} \rightarrow sin\,\theta = \frac{1}{3}$. $cos\,\theta = \frac{base}{hypotenuse} \rightarrow cos\,\theta = \frac{6}{12} = \frac{1}{2} \rightarrow cos\,\theta = \frac{1}{2}$.

Example 2. Find the value of $tan\,\theta$ if $sin\,\theta = \frac{10}{3}$ and $cos\,\theta = \frac{4}{3}$.

Solution: We know that $sin\,\theta = \frac{perpendicular}{hypotenuse}$, $cos\,\theta = \frac{base}{hypotenuse}$, and $tan\,\theta = \frac{perpendicular}{base}$. According to the question, we have a trigonometric ratio of $sin\,\theta$, and $cos\,\theta$. So, we can use the numerator to find the trigonometric ratio of $tan\,\theta$: $sin\,\theta = \frac{perpendicular}{hypotenuse} = \frac{10}{3}$, and $cos\,\theta = \frac{base}{hypotenuse} = \frac{4}{3} \rightarrow tan\,\theta = \frac{perpendicular}{base} = \frac{10}{4} = \frac{5}{2}$.

Solving Right Triangles

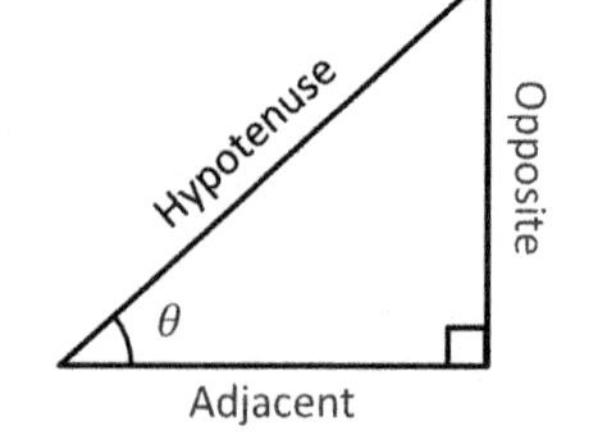

- By using Sine, Cosine, or Tangent, we can find an unknown side in a right triangle when we have one length, and one angle (Apart from the right angle).
- Adjacent, Opposite, and Hypotenuse, in a right triangle are shown below.
- Recall the three main trigonometric functions:

  SOH–CAH–TOA, $sin\,\theta = \frac{opposite}{hypotenuse}$, $cos\,\theta = \frac{adjacent}{hypotenuse}$, $tan\,\theta = \frac{opposite}{adjacent}$.

Examples:

Example 1. Find AC in the following triangle. Round answers to the nearest tenth.

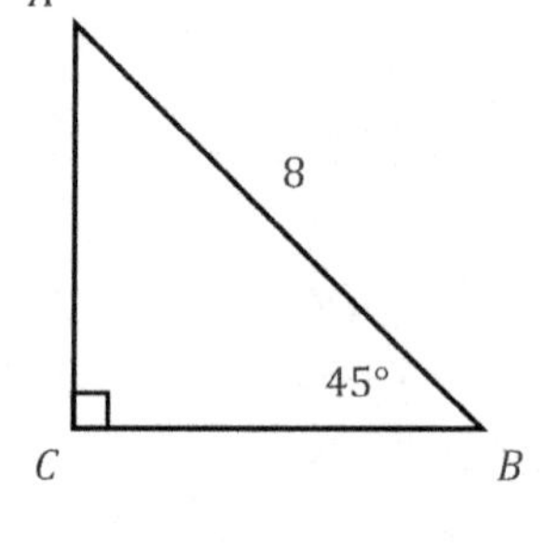

Solution: Considering that: $sin\,\theta = \frac{opposite}{hypotenuse}$.

Therefore: $sin\,45° = \frac{AC}{8} \rightarrow 8 \times sin\,45° = AC$,

Now, use a calculator to find $sin\,45°$.

$sin\,45° = \frac{\sqrt{2}}{2} \cong 0.70710$.

Then:

$AC = 8 \times 0.70710 = 5.6568 = 5.7$

Example 2. If $tan\,\alpha = \frac{3}{4}$, then $sin\,\alpha =$?

Solution: We know that: $tan\,\theta = \frac{opposite}{adjacent}$, and $tan\,\alpha = \frac{3}{4}$.

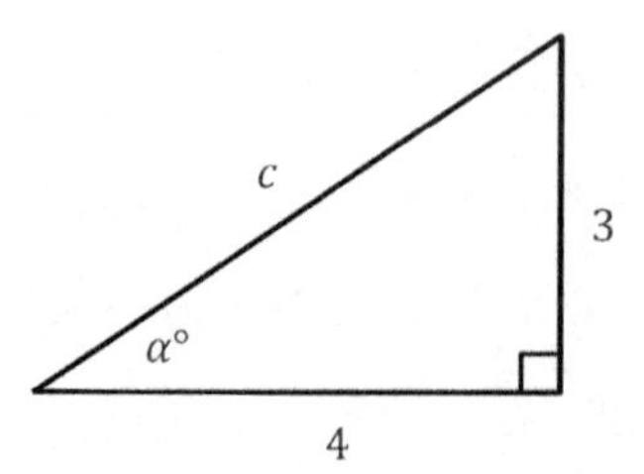

Therefore, the opposite side of the angle α is 3 and the adjacent side is 4. Let's draw the triangle.

Using the Pythagorean theorem, we have:

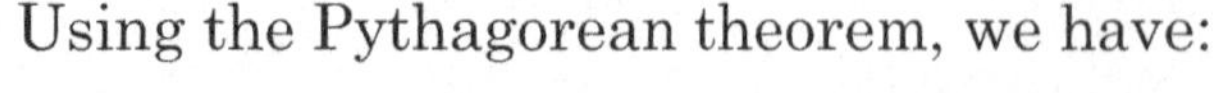

$a^2 + b^2 = c^2 \rightarrow 3^2 + 4^2 = c^2 \rightarrow 9 + 16 = c^2 \rightarrow c = 5$.

Then:

$sin\,\alpha = \frac{opposite}{hypotenuse} = \frac{3}{5}$.

Special Right Triangles

- Special right triangles are specific right triangles with fixed angle measures and predictable side length ratios. The two main types are the $30-60-90$ and $45-45-90$ triangles.
  - $30-60-90$ triangle: Angles are $30°$, $60°$, and $90°$, with side ratios of $1:\sqrt{3}:2$. Trigonometric ratios are easily calculated:
$$sin(30°)=\frac{1}{2}, cos(30°)=\frac{\sqrt{3}}{2}, tan(30°)=\frac{1}{\sqrt{3}}=\frac{\sqrt{3}}{3}$$
$$sin(60°)=\frac{\sqrt{3}}{2}, cos(60°)=\frac{1}{2}, tan(60°)=\sqrt{3}$$
  - $45-45-90$ triangle: Angles are $45°$, $45°$, and $90°$, with equal legs and a hypotenuse of leg length multiplied by $\sqrt{2}$. Trigonometric ratios are:
$$sin(45°)=cos(45°)=\frac{1}{\sqrt{2}} \text{ or } \frac{\sqrt{2}}{2}$$
$$tan(45°)=1$$
- These special triangles simplify trigonometric calculations and serve as a foundation for understanding more complex problems in geometry, algebra, and calculus.

Example:

Find AC and BC in the following triangle. Round answers to the nearest tenth.

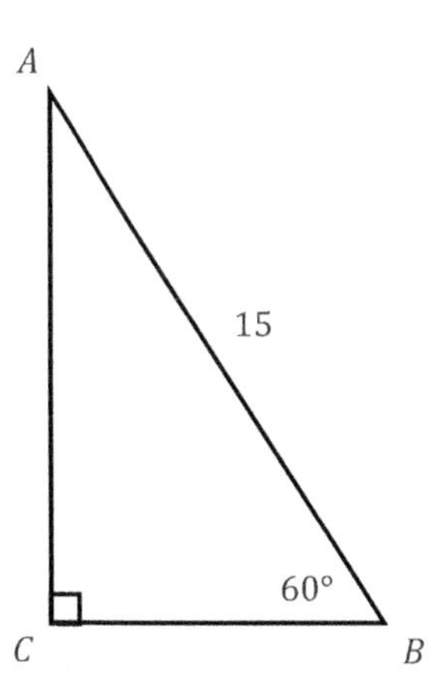

Solution: Considering that: $sin\,\theta=\frac{opposite}{hypotenuse}$.

Therefore: $sin\,60°=\frac{AC}{15}\rightarrow 15\times sin\,60°=AC$

$$\rightarrow AC=15\times\frac{\sqrt{3}}{2}=12.99=13.$$

According to the figure, triangle ABC is a $30-60-90$ triangle and the ratio of its sides is $1:\sqrt{3}:2$. Therefore, the length of side BC is half the length of AB:

$BC=\frac{1}{2}\times 15=7.5.$

Chapter 2: Practices

Solve.

1) In a right triangle, the length of one leg is 5 units and the hypotenuse is 13 units. Find the length of the other leg using the Pythagorean Theorem.
2) A rectangular garden has dimensions of 12 meters by 16 meters. A diagonal path is to be constructed from one corner of the garden to the opposite corner. What is the length of the diagonal path?
   Hint: Utilize the Pythagorean Theorem to find the length of the diagonal path.
3) A ladder is leaning against a wall. The ladder is 17 meters long, and the base of the ladder is 8 meters away from the wall. How high on the wall does the ladder reach?
4) A right-angled triangle has one leg measuring 15 units and the other leg measuring 20 units. Calculate the length of the hypotenuse using the Pythagorean Theorem.

Find the given trigonometric ratio.

5) $tan\, O =$ ____

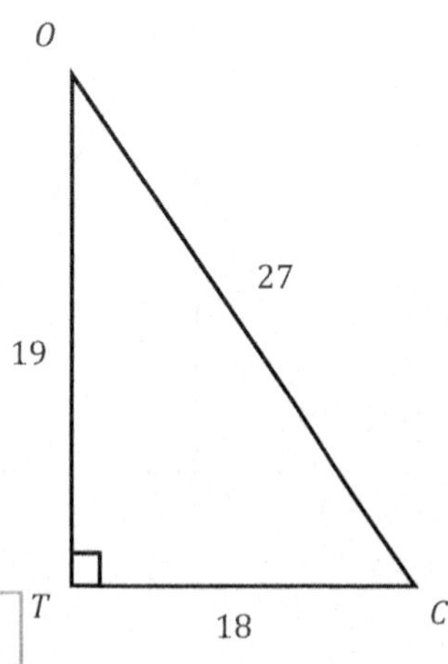

6) $sin\, X =$ ____

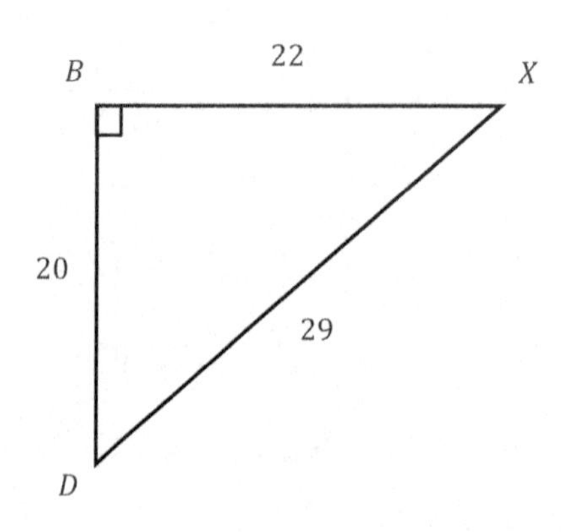

7) $cos\, X =$ ____

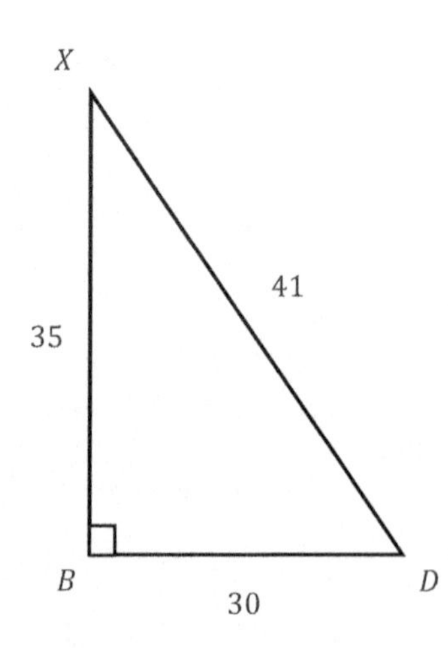

Find the measure of each angle indicated.

8)

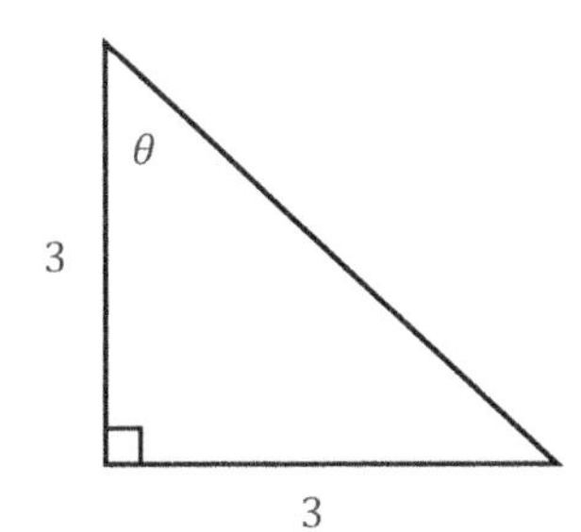

9)

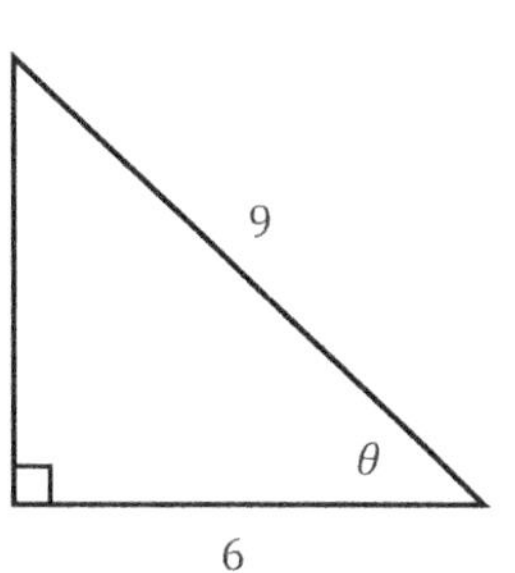

Find the missing sides. Round answers to the nearest tenth.

10)

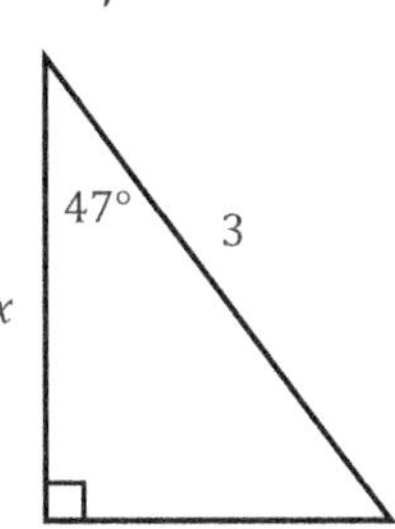

11)

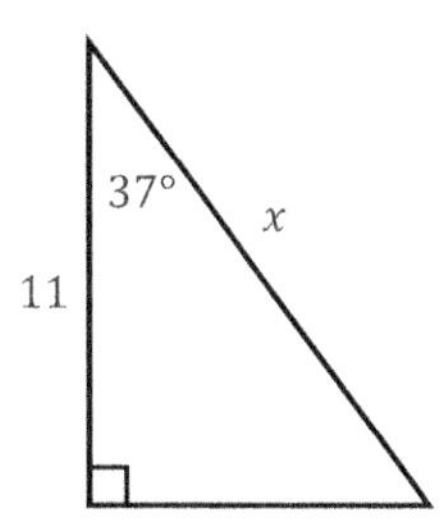

12)

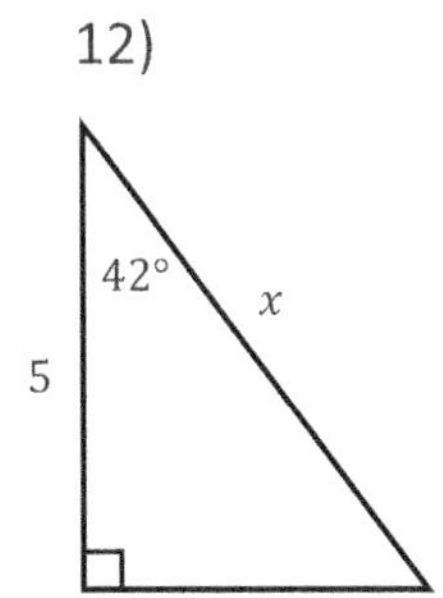

13)

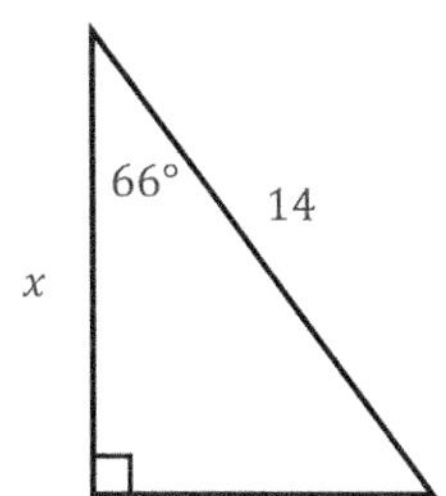

Find the value of x and y in the following special right triangles.

14)

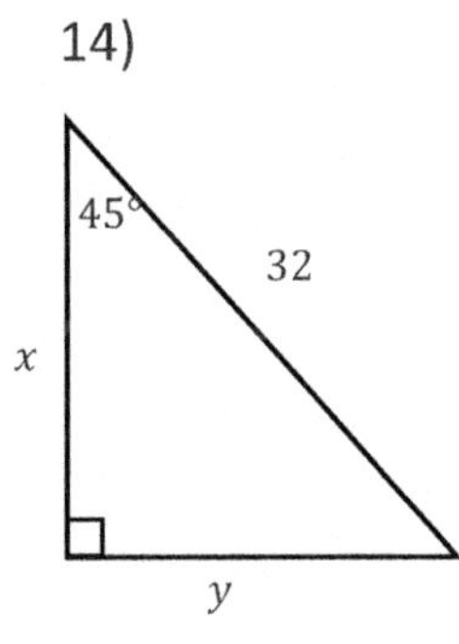

15)

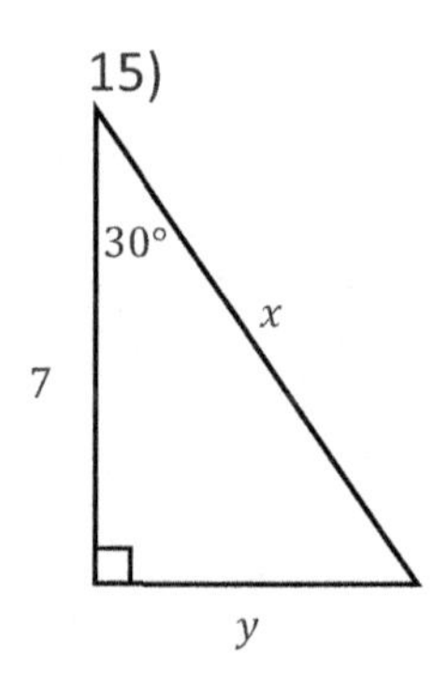

16)

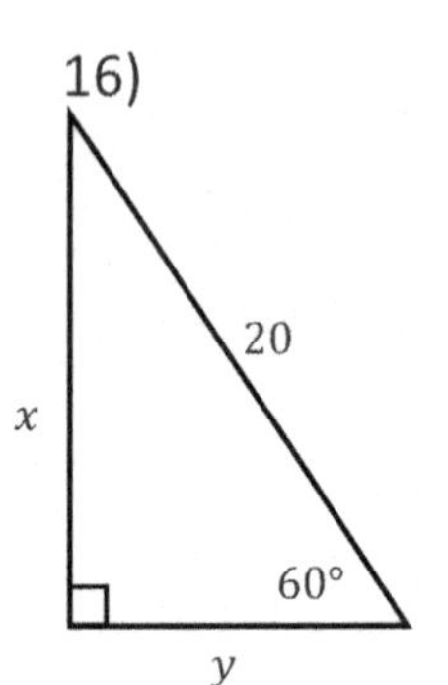

17)

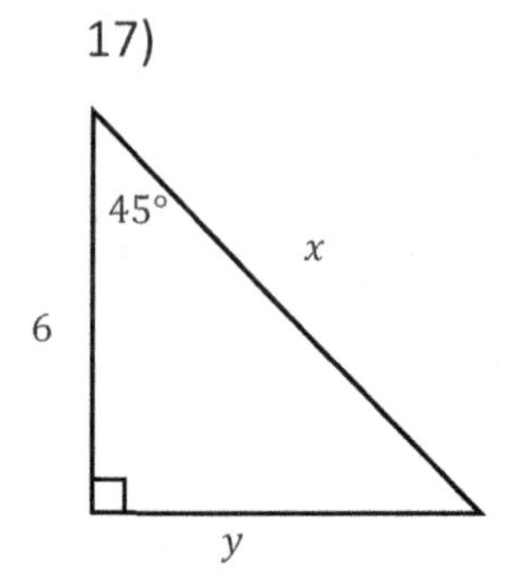

Chapter 2: Answers

1) 12
2) 20
3) 15
4) 25
5) $\frac{18}{19}$
6) $\frac{20}{29}$
7) $\frac{35}{41}$
8) 45°
9) 48.19°
10) 2
11) 13.8
12) 6.7
13) 5.7
14) $x = y = \frac{32}{\sqrt{2}}$ or $16\sqrt{2}$
15) $x = \frac{14\sqrt{3}}{3}$, $y = \frac{7\sqrt{3}}{3}$
16) $x = 10\sqrt{3}$, $y = 10$
17) $x = 6\sqrt{2}$, $y = 6$

CHAPTER

3 Trigonometric Functions

Math topics that you'll learn in this chapter:

- ☑ Sine, Cosine, and Tangent
- ☑ Reciprocal Functions: Cosecant, Secant, and Cotangent
- ☑ Domain and Range of Trigonometric Functions
- ☑ Trigonometric Function Values for Key Angles
- ☑ The Unit Circle

Sine, Cosine, and Tangent

- Sine, cosine, and tangent are fundamental trigonometric functions used in mathematics to relate the angles of a right triangle to the lengths of its sides. These functions are essential for understanding various mathematical concepts, including geometry, calculus, and physics.
  - ***Sine*** (sin): The sine function relates the ratio of the length of the side opposite to an angle in a right triangle to the length of the hypotenuse (the longest side). It is defined as $sin(\theta) = \frac{opposite}{hypotenuse}$, where θ is the angle.
  - ***Cosine*** (cos): The cosine function relates the ratio of the length of the side adjacent to an angle in a right triangle to the length of the hypotenuse. It is defined as $cos(\theta) = \frac{adjacent}{hypotenuse}$, where θ is the angle.
  - ***Tangent*** (tan): The tangent function relates the ratio of the sine function to the cosine function or the ratio of the length of the side opposite to an angle in a right triangle to the length of the side adjacent to the angle. It is defined as $tan(\theta) = \frac{sin(\theta)}{cos(\theta)}$ or $\frac{opposite}{adjacent}$, where θ is the angle.
- These functions are widely used in various applications, including solving problems involving right triangles, graphing periodic functions, and analyzing real-world phenomena like waves, vibrations, and oscillations.

Example:

Find the value of sine, cosine, and tangent of the angle $\widehat{BAC}$ in the figure below.

Solution: According to the size of the sides of the triangle and using the sine, cosine, and tangent formulas, we will have:

$$sin(\theta) = \frac{opposite}{hypotenuse} = \frac{6.81}{10.5} \cong 0.65$$

$$cos(\theta) = \frac{adjacent}{hypotenuse} = \frac{8}{10.5} \cong 0.76$$

$$tan(\theta) = \frac{opposite}{adjacent} = \frac{6.81}{8} \cong 0.85$$

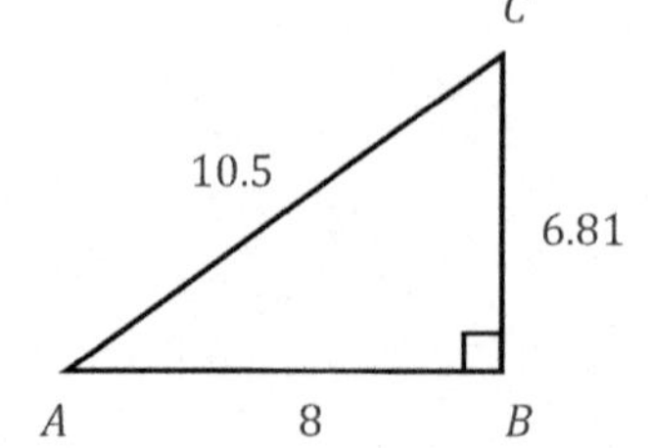

Reciprocal Functions: Cosecant, Secant, and Cotangent

- The trigonometric functions that can be defined in terms of $\sin\theta$, $\cos\theta$, and $\tan\theta$ are called the reciprocal functions.
- The secant function is the set of ordered pairs $(\theta, \sec\theta)$ for all θ for which $\cos\theta \neq 0$, $\sec\theta = \frac{1}{\cos\theta}$.
- The set of secant function values is the set of real numbers that is $\{x: x \geq 1 \text{ or } x \leq -1\}$.
- The cosecant function is the set of ordered pairs $(\theta, \csc\theta)$ for all θ for which $\sin\theta \neq 0$, $\csc\theta = \frac{1}{\sin\theta}$.
- The set of cosecant function values is the set of real numbers that is $\{x: x \geq 1 \text{ or } x \leq -1\}$.
- The cotangent function is the set of ordered pairs $(\theta, \cot\theta)$ that for all θ for which $\tan\theta$ is defined and not equal to 0, $\cot\theta = \frac{1}{\tan\theta}$, and for all θ for which $\tan\theta$ is not defined, $\cot\theta = 0$.
- The set of cotangent function values is the set of real numbers.

Examples:

Example 1. Find the value of $\sec\theta$ if $\cos\theta = \frac{2}{7}$ using the reciprocal identity.

Solution: The reciprocal identity of *sec* is: $\sec\theta = \frac{1}{\cos\theta}$.
If $\cos\theta = \frac{2}{7}$, then $\sec\theta = \frac{1}{\frac{2}{7}} = \frac{7}{2}$.

Example 2. Simplify the function $\tan(\theta)\cot(\theta)\sin(\theta)$.

Solution: The reciprocal identity of $\cot\theta$: $\cot\theta = \frac{1}{\tan(\theta)}$.

$$\tan(\theta)\cot(\theta)\sin(\theta) = \tan(\theta) \times \frac{1}{\tan(\theta)} \times \sin(\theta) = \sin\theta$$

Domain and Range of Trigonometric Functions

- The domain of the sine function and cosine function is the set of real numbers.
- The range of the sine function and cosine function is the set of real numbers $[-1, 1]$.
- The domain of the tangent function is the set of real numbers except for $\frac{\pi}{2} + n\pi$ for all integral values of n.
- The range of the tangent function is the set of all real numbers.
- The domain of the cotangent function is the set of real numbers except for $n\pi$ for all integral values of n.
- The range of the cotangent function is the set of all real numbers.
- The domain of the secant function is the set of real numbers except for $\frac{\pi}{2} + n\pi$ for all integral values of n.
- The range of the secant function is the set of real numbers $(-\infty, -1] \cup [1, +\infty)$.
- The domain of the cosecant function is the set of real numbers except for $n\pi$ for all integral values of n.
- The range of the cosecant function is the set of real numbers $(-\infty, -1] \cup [1, +\infty)$.

Examples:

Example 1. Find the range of $y = 4\tan x$.

Solution: The range of $y = 4\tan x$ is $(-\infty, +\infty)$.

Example 2. Find the domain and range of $y = \sin x - 4$.

Solution: The range of $\sin x$ is $[-1,1]$.

$-1 \le \sin x \le 1 \Rightarrow -1 - 4 \le \sin x - 4 \le 1 - 4 \Rightarrow -5 \le y \le -3$

The domain is $(-\infty, +\infty)$.

Example 3. Find the domain of $y = 3\cos x + 4$.

Solution: The domain of $y = 3\cos x + 4$ is $(-\infty, +\infty)$.

Trigonometric Function Values for Key Angles

- It is useful to remember the exact values of the trigonometric function summarized below:

θ	$0°$	$30°$	$45°$	$60°$	$90°$
$\sin\theta$	0	$\frac{1}{2}$	$\frac{\sqrt{2}}{2}$	$\frac{\sqrt{3}}{2}$	1
$\cos\theta$	1	$\frac{\sqrt{3}}{2}$	$\frac{\sqrt{2}}{2}$	$\frac{1}{2}$	0
$\tan\theta$	0	$\frac{\sqrt{3}}{3}$	1	$\sqrt{3}$	undefined

Examples:

Example 1. Find the exact value of $\sec 45°$.

Solution: We know that $\sec\theta = \frac{1}{\cos\theta}$.

$$\sec 45° = \frac{1}{\cos 45°} = \frac{1}{\frac{\sqrt{2}}{2}} = \frac{2}{\sqrt{2}}$$

$$= \frac{2}{\sqrt{2}} \times \frac{\sqrt{2}}{\sqrt{2}} = \frac{2\sqrt{2}}{2} = \sqrt{2}$$

Example 2. Find the value of $\sin 30° \cos 60°$.

Solution: $\sin 30° = \frac{1}{2}$ and $\cos 60° = \frac{1}{2}$.

$$\sin 30° \cos 60° = \frac{1}{2} \times \frac{1}{2} = \frac{1}{4}$$

Example 3. Find the value of $\cos 30° + \tan 0° + \sin 60°$.

Solution: $\cos 30° = \frac{\sqrt{3}}{2}$, $\tan 0° = 0$ and $\sin 60° = \frac{\sqrt{3}}{2}$.

$$\cos 30° + \tan 0° + \sin 60° = \frac{\sqrt{3}}{2} + 0 + \frac{\sqrt{3}}{2} = \sqrt{3}$$

The Unit Circle

- The unit circle is a circle with a center at the origin and a radius of 1 and has the equation $x^2 + y^2 = 1$.

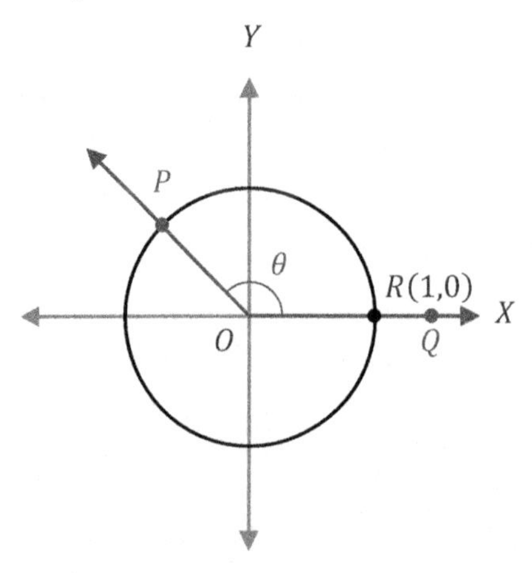

- If $\angle POQ$ is an angle in standard position and P is the point that the terminal side of the angle intersects the unit circle and $m\angle POQ = \theta$. Then:
  - The sine function is a set of ordered pairs $(\theta, \sin\theta)$ that $\sin\theta$ is the y coordinate of P.
  - The cosine function is the set of ordered pairs $(\theta, \cos\theta)$ that $\cos\theta$ is the x −coordinate of P.

Examples:

Example 1. If $P\left(\frac{\sqrt{3}}{2}, -\frac{1}{2}\right)$ is a point on the unit circle and the terminal side of an angle in a standard position whose size is θ. Find $\sin\theta$ and $\cos\theta$.

Solution:

$\sin\theta = y$ −coordinate of $P = -\frac{1}{2}$.

$\cos\theta = x$ −coordinate of $P = \frac{\sqrt{3}}{2}$.

Example 2. Does point $P\left(\frac{1}{4}, \frac{1}{4}\right)$ lie on the unit circle?

Solution: The equation of a unit circle is: $x^2 + y^2 = 1$. Now substitute $x = \frac{1}{4}$ and $y = \frac{1}{4}$:

$$\left(\frac{1}{4}\right)^2 + \left(\frac{1}{4}\right)^2 = \frac{1}{8} \neq 1$$

Since, $x^2 + y^2 \neq 1$, the point $P\left(\frac{1}{4}, \frac{1}{4}\right)$ does not lie on the unit circle.

Chapter 3: Practices

Find the value of sine, cosine, and tangent of the angle γ in the following figures.

1)

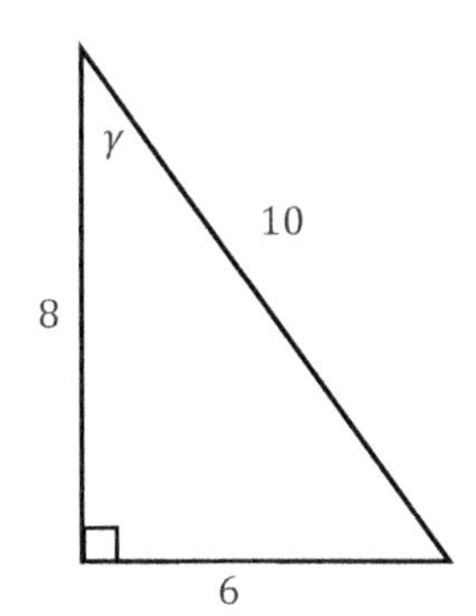

2)

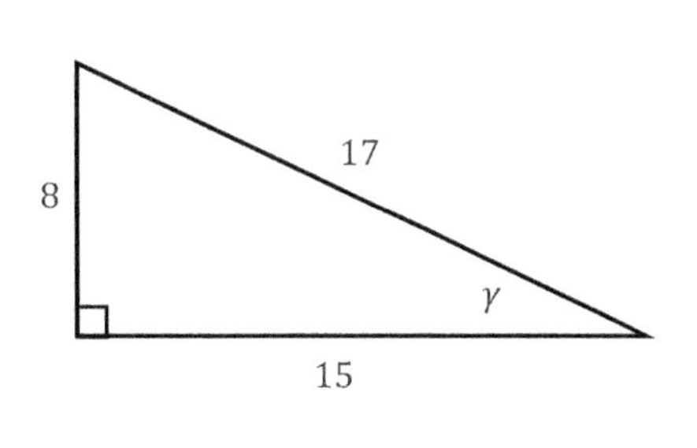

3)

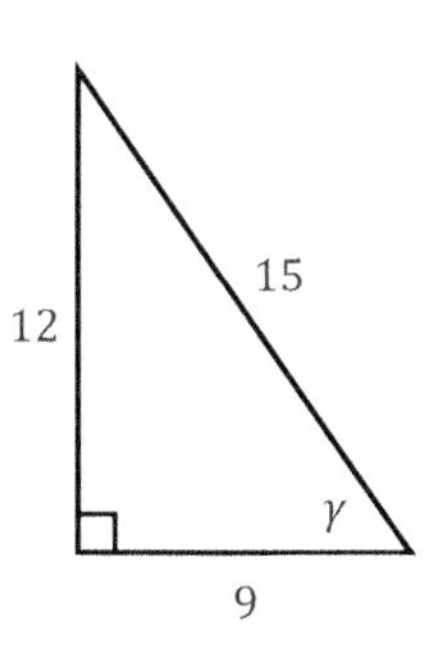

Solve.

4) Find the value of $sec\, x$ if $cos\, x = \frac{3}{5}$ using the reciprocal identity. _______

5) Find the value of $csc\, x$ if $sin\, x = \frac{2}{3}$ using the reciprocal identity. _______

Find the domain and range of functions.

6) $y = cos\, x - 4$

Domain: _______

Range: _______

7) $y = sin\, x - 3$

Domain: _______

Range: _______

8) $y = \frac{1}{2 - sin\, 2x}$

Domain: _______

Range: _______

9) $y = 2\, cos\, x + 6$

Domain: _______

Range: _______

Find the exact value of angles.

10) $sec\, 120°$

11) $csc\, 60°$

12) $sin\, 45°\, cos\, 30°$

13) $cos\, 60° + tan\, 30° + sin\, 30°$

Solve.

14) If $P\left(-\frac{\sqrt{3}}{2}, \frac{1}{2}\right)$ is a point on the unit circle and the terminal side of an angle in a standard position whose size is θ. Find $\sin\theta$ and $\cos\theta$. _______

15) If $P\left(\frac{\sqrt{2}}{2}, -\frac{\sqrt{2}}{2}\right)$ is a point on the unit circle and the terminal side of an angle in a standard po sition whose size is θ. Find $\sin\theta$ and $\cos\theta$. _______

Chapter 3: Answers

1) $\sin\gamma=\frac{3}{5}, \cos\gamma=\frac{4}{5}, \tan\gamma=\frac{3}{2}$
2) $\sin\gamma=\frac{8}{17}, \cos\gamma=\frac{15}{17}, \tan\gamma=\frac{8}{15}$
3) $\sin\gamma=\frac{4}{5}, \cos\gamma=\frac{3}{5}, \tan\gamma=\frac{4}{3}$
4) $\frac{5}{3}$
5) $\frac{3}{2}$
6) Domain: $(-\infty,+\infty)$

   Range: $[-5,-3]$
7) Domain: $(-\infty,+\infty)$

   Range: $[-4,-2]$
8) Domain: $(-\infty,+\infty)$

   Range: $\left[\frac{1}{3},1\right]$
9) Domain: $(-\infty,+\infty)$

   Range: $[4,8]$
10) -2
11) $\frac{2\sqrt{3}}{3}$
12) $\frac{\sqrt{6}}{4}$
13) $1+\frac{\sqrt{3}}{3}$
14) $\sin\theta=\frac{1}{2}$

    $\cos\theta=-\frac{\sqrt{3}}{2}$
15) $\sin\theta=-\frac{\sqrt{2}}{2}$

    $\cos\theta=\frac{\sqrt{2}}{2}$

CHAPTER

4 Trigonometric Identities

Math topics that you'll learn in this chapter:

- ☑ Fundamental Trigonometric Identities
- ☑ Pythagorean Trigonometric Identities
- ☑ Co-Function, Even-Odd, and Periodicity Identities
- ☑ Double Angle and Half-Angle Formulas
- ☑ Sum and Difference Formulas
- ☑ Product-to-Sum and Sum-to-Product Formulas

Fundamental Trigonometric Identities

- The following equations are important trigonometric identities:
  - $tan\,\theta = \frac{sin\,\theta}{cos\,\theta}$
  - $cot\,\theta = \frac{cos\,\theta}{sin\,\theta}$
  - $csc\,\theta = \frac{1}{sin\,\theta}$
  - $sec\,\theta = \frac{1}{cos\,\theta}$
  - $cot\,\theta = \frac{1}{tan\,\theta}$
  - $cos^2\,\theta + sin^2\,\theta = 1$
  - $sin^2\,\theta = 1 - cos^2\,\theta$
  - $cos^2\,\theta = 1 - sin^2\,\theta$
  - $tan^2\,\theta + 1 = sec^2\,\theta$
  - $1 + cot^2\,\theta = csc^2\,\theta$
- You can use fundamental identities to rewrite trigonometric expressions in terms of a single trigonometric function.

Examples:

Example 1. Confirm the identity $cos\,\theta + sin\,\theta\,tan\,\theta = sec\,\theta$.

Solution: You can use fundamental trigonometric identities to solve this problem:

$(cos\,\theta) + (sin\,\theta)\left(\frac{sin\,\theta}{cos\,\theta}\right) = sec\,\theta$

$\frac{cos^2\,\theta + sin^2\,\theta}{cos\,\theta} = sec\,\theta$

$\frac{1}{cos\,\theta} = sec\,\theta$

$sec\,\theta = sec\,\theta.$

Example 2. Find the value of $tan\,\theta$ using $cot\,\theta = \frac{3}{5}$.

Solution: Use fundamental trigonometric identities to solve this problem:

$cot\,\theta = \frac{1}{tan\,\theta}$, and $\frac{3}{5} = \frac{1}{tan\,\theta} \rightarrow tan\,\theta = \frac{1}{\frac{3}{5}} = \frac{5}{3}$.

Pythagorean Trigonometric Identities

- An identity is an equation that is true for all variable values for which the variable expressions are defined.
- Since the identity $sin^2\theta + cos^2\theta = 1$ is based on the Pythagorean theorem, we refer to it as the Pythagorean identity.
- Two related Pythagorean identities can be written by dividing both sides of the equation by the same expression:
  - $1 + tan^2\theta = sec^2\theta$
  - $cot^2\theta + 1 = csc^2\theta$

Examples:

Example 1. Verify that $sin^2\frac{\pi}{4} + cos^2\frac{\pi}{4} = 1$.

Solution: $cos\frac{\pi}{4} = \frac{\sqrt{2}}{2}$ and $sin\frac{\pi}{4} = \frac{\sqrt{2}}{2}$:

$sin^2\frac{\pi}{4} + cos^2\frac{\pi}{4} = \left(\frac{\sqrt{2}}{2}\right)^2 + \left(\frac{\sqrt{2}}{2}\right)^2 = \frac{1}{2} + \frac{1}{2} = 1$

Example 2. If $cos\,x = \frac{3}{5}$ and x is in the 1st quadrant, find $sin\,x$.

Solution: Use Pythagorean identity:

$sin^2 x = 1 - cos^2 x$

$sin(x) = \pm\sqrt{1 - cos^2(x)} = \pm\sqrt{1 - \left(\frac{3}{5}\right)^2} = \pm\frac{4}{5}$

Since x is in the first quadrant, $sin\,x$ is positive. So $sin\,x = \frac{4}{5}$.

Example 3. Use a Pythagorean identity to simplify the $14 + 5\,cos^2(x) + 5\,sin^2(x)$.

Solution: The Pythagorean identity is $sin^2\theta + cos^2\theta = 1$.

$14 + 5\,cos^2(x) + 5\,sin^2(x) = 14 + 5\big(cos^2(x) + sin^2(x)\big)$

$= 14 + 5(1) = 19.$

bit.ly/46ssoBn

Find more at

Co-Function, Even-Odd, and Periodicity Identities

- **Co-Function Identities:** Co-Function identities describe the relationship between sine, cosine, and other trigonometric functions. They are derived from complementary angles (two angles whose sum equals 90 degrees). The Co-Function Identities are as follows:

  $sin(90° - x) = cos(x)$ $\quad$ $cot(90° - x) = tan(x)$
  $cos(90° - x) = sin(x)$ $\quad$ $sec(90° - x) = csc(x)$
  $tan(90° - x) = cot(x)$ $\quad$ $csc(90° - x) = sec(x)$

- **Even-Odd Identities:** Even-Odd identities describe the behavior of trigonometric functions with respect to the input sign. A function is even if $f(x) = f(-x)$, and it's odd if $f(x) = -f(-x)$. The Even-Odd Identities are as follows:

  $sin(-x) = -sin(x)$ (Sine is an odd function)
  $cos(-x) = cos(x)$ (Cosine is an even function)
  $tan(-x) = -tan(x)$ (Tangent is an odd function)
  $cot(-x) = -cot(x)$ (Cotangent is an odd function)
  $sec(-x) = sec(x)$ (Secant is an even function)
  $csc(-x) = -csc(x)$ (Cosecant is an odd function)

- **Periodicity Identities:** Periodicity identities describe the behavior of trigonometric functions when their input is incremented by a specific value called the period. A function is periodic if $f(x + P) = f(x)$ for all x, where P is the period. The Periodicity Identities are as follows:

  $sin(x + 2\pi n) = sin(x)$ for all integers n (sine has a period of 2π)
  $cos(x + 2\pi n) = cos(x)$ for all integers n (cosine has a period of 2π)
  $tan(x + \pi n) = tan(x)$ for all integers n (tangent has a period of π)
  $cot(x + \pi n) = cot(x)$ for all integers n (cotangent has a period of π)
  $sec(x + 2\pi n) = sec(x)$ for all integers n (secant has a period of 2π)
  $csc(x + 2\pi n) = csc(x)$ for all integers n (cosecant has a period of 2π)

Examples:

Example 1. Find the value of $tan\,120°$ using co-function identities.

Solution: Use co-function identity, $cot(90° - x) = tan(x)$.

$tan\,120° = cot(90° - 120°) = cot(-30°) = -cot\,30° = -\sqrt{3}$.

Example 2. Use the concept of periodicity to solve this problem. Find the exact value of $cos\left(\frac{15\pi}{6}\right)$ using the periodicity identity of the cosine function.

Solution: Using the periodicity of the cosine function, we can simplify $\frac{15\pi}{6}$ to $\frac{\pi}{2}$, $\left(\frac{15\pi}{6} - 2\pi = \frac{\pi}{2}\right)$. Thus, $cos\left(\frac{15\pi}{6}\right) = cos\left(\frac{\pi}{2}\right) = 0$.

Double Angle and Half-Angle Formulas

- Double-angle formulas are used for trigonometric ratios of double angles in terms of trigonometric ratios of single angles.
- The double-angle formulas are as follows:
  - $\sin 2\theta = 2\sin\theta\cos\theta$
  - $\sin 2\theta = \frac{2\tan\theta}{1+\tan^2\theta}$
  - $\cos 2\theta = \cos^2\theta - \sin^2\theta$
  - $\cos 2\theta = 1 - 2\sin^2\theta$
  - $\cos 2\theta = 2\cos^2\theta - 1$
  - $\cos 2\theta = \frac{1-\tan^2\theta}{1+\tan^2\theta}$
  - $\tan 2\theta = \frac{2\tan\theta}{1-\tan^2\theta}$
- The half-angle formulas are as follows:
  - $\sin\frac{\theta}{2} = \pm\sqrt{\frac{1-\cos\theta}{2}}$
  - $\cos\frac{\theta}{2} = \pm\sqrt{\frac{1+\cos\theta}{2}}$
  - $\tan\frac{\theta}{2} = \pm\sqrt{\frac{1-\cos\theta}{1+\cos\theta}} = \frac{\sin\theta}{1+\cos\theta} = \frac{1-\cos\theta}{\sin\theta}$

Examples:

Example 1. If $\tan\theta = \frac{4}{3}$, find the values of $\cos 2\theta$.

Solution: Use the double-angle formulas:

$$\cos 2\theta = \frac{1-\tan^2\theta}{1+\tan^2\theta} = \frac{1-\left(\frac{4}{3}\right)^2}{1+\left(\frac{4}{3}\right)^2} = \frac{1-\frac{16}{9}}{1+\frac{16}{9}} = \frac{-\frac{7}{9}}{\frac{25}{9}} = -\frac{7}{25}$$

Example 2. If $\cos\theta = \frac{1}{2}$, find the values of $\sin\frac{\theta}{2}$.

Solution: Use the half-angle formulas:

$$\sin\frac{\theta}{2} = \pm\sqrt{\frac{1-\cos\theta}{2}} = \pm\sqrt{\frac{1-\frac{1}{2}}{2}} = \pm\sqrt{\frac{\frac{1}{2}}{2}} = \pm\sqrt{\frac{1}{4}} = \pm\frac{1}{2}$$

Sum and Difference Formulas

- The sum and difference formulas in trigonometry are used to find the value of trigonometric functions at certain angles.
- These formulas help us evaluate the value of trigonometric functions at angles that can be expressed as the sum or difference of certain angles 0°, 30°, 45°, 60°, 90°, and 180°.
- The sum and difference formulas are as follows:
  - $sin(A+B) = sin\,A\,cos\,B + cos\,A\,sin\,B$
  - $sin(A-B) = sin\,A\,cos\,B - cos\,A\,sin\,B$
  - $cos(A+B) = cos\,A\,cos\,B - sin\,A\,sin\,B$
  - $cos(A-B) = cos\,A\,cos\,B + sin\,A\,sin\,B$
  - $tan(A+B) = \frac{tan(A)+tan(B)}{1-tan(A)\,tan(B)}$
  - $tan(A-B) = \frac{tan(A)-tan(B)}{1-tan(A)\,tan(B)}$

Examples:

Example 1. Find the value of $sin(120° + 45°)$.

Solution: Use the sum and difference formula:

$$sin(120° + 45°) = sin(120°)\,cos(45°) + cos(120°)\,sin(45°)$$
$$= \left(\frac{\sqrt{3}}{2}\right)\left(\frac{\sqrt{2}}{2}\right) + \left(-\frac{1}{2}\right)\left(\frac{\sqrt{2}}{2}\right)$$
$$= \frac{\sqrt{6}}{4} - \frac{\sqrt{2}}{4} = \frac{\sqrt{6}-\sqrt{2}}{4}.$$

Example 2. Find the value of $cos\,105°$.

Solution: Use the sum and difference formula:

$$cos\,105° = cos(60° + 45°) = cos\,60°\,cos\,45° - sin\,60°\,sin\,45°$$
$$= \left(\frac{1}{2}\right)\left(\frac{\sqrt{2}}{2}\right) - \left(\frac{\sqrt{3}}{2}\right)\left(\frac{\sqrt{2}}{2}\right) = \frac{\sqrt{2}-\sqrt{6}}{4}.$$

Product-to-Sum and Sum-to-Product Formulas

- The Product-to-Sum and Sum-to-Product formulas are trigonometric identities that help convert products of sine and cosine functions into sums or differences of these functions, and vice versa. These identities are particularly useful for simplifying trigonometric expressions, solving trigonometric equations, and in areas such as Fourier analysis, signal processing, and calculus.
  1) **Product-to-Sum Formulas:** These formulas help convert products of sines and cosines into sums or differences of sines and cosines. The formulas are as follows:
     - $sin(A)\,sin(B) = \frac{1}{2}[cos(A-B) - cos(A+B)]$
     - $cos(A)\,cos(B) = \frac{1}{2}[cos(A-B) + cos(A+B)]$
     - $sin(A)\,cos(B) = \frac{1}{2}[sin(A+B) + sin(A-B)]$
  2) **Sum-to-Product Formulas:** These formulas help convert sums or differences of sines and cosines into products of sines and cosines. The formulas are as follows:
     - $sin(A) + sin(B) = 2\ sin\left(\frac{A+B}{2}\right) cos\left(\frac{A-B}{2}\right)$
     - $sin(A) - sin(B) = 2\,cos\left(\frac{A+B}{2}\right) sin\left(\frac{A-B}{2}\right)$
     - $cos(A) + cos(B) = 2\,cos\left(\frac{A+B}{2}\right) cos\left(\frac{A-B}{2}\right)$
     - $cos(A) - cos(B) = -2\ sin\left(\frac{A+B}{2}\right) sin\left(\frac{A-B}{2}\right)$

Example:

How can the product-to-sum formula be applied to express $sin(2x)cos(3x)$ as a sum?

Solution: To express $sin(2x)cos(3x)$ as a sum using the product-to-sum formula, we can use the following identity: $sin(A)\,cos(B) = \frac{1}{2}[sin(A+B) + sin(A-B)]$

Substituting $2x$ for A and $3x$ for B, we get:

$$sin(2x)\,cos(3x) = \left(\frac{1}{2}\right)[sin(5x) + sin(-x)]$$

Since $sin(-x) = -sin(x)$, we can simplify the above equation as:

$$sin(2x)\,cos(3x) = \left(\frac{1}{2}\right)[sin(5x) - sin(x)]$$

Therefore, $sin(2x)\,cos(3x)$ can be expressed as the difference between two sine functions, which are $\left(\frac{1}{2}\right) sin(5x)$ and $-(\frac{1}{2})sin\ (x)$.

Chapter 4: Practices

Simplify each expression using fundamental trigonometric identities.

1) $cot\,x\,sec\,x\,sin\,x =$ _____

2) $sin\,x\,cos^2\,x - sin\,x =$ _____

3) $tan^3\,x\,csc^3\,x =$ _____

4) $\frac{tan\,x}{sec\,x} =$ _____

Simplify each trigonometric expression using Pythagorean identities.

5) $(sin\,x + cos\,x)^2 =$ _____

6) $(1 + cot^2\,x)\,sin^2\,x =$ _____

7) $csc^2\,x - cot^2\,x =$ _____

8) $2\,sin^2\,x + cos^2\,x =$ _____

Solve using cofunction identities.

9) $sin\,x = cos\,35°$

10) $cot\,x = tan\,80°$

11) $csc\,68° = sec\,x$

12) $sec(3x) = csc(x + 22°)$

Solve using Even-Odd identities.

13) $sin(-30°) =$ _____

14) $cot(-45°) =$ _____

15) $sec(-60°) =$ _____

16) $csc(-45°) =$ _____

Solve using periodicity identities.

17) $sin\frac{22\pi}{3}$

18) $tan\frac{17\pi}{2}$

19) $cos\frac{25\pi}{4}$

20) $sin\frac{14\pi}{3}$

Solve.

21) If $\sin(\theta) = \frac{2}{5}$ and θ is in the second quadrant, find exact values for $\cos(2\theta)$.

22) If $cos(\theta) = \frac{4}{5}$ and θ is in the fourth quadrant, find exact values for $sin(2\theta)$.

23) Use a half-angle identity to find the exact value of each expression.

$cos\ 30° =$

$cos\ 105° =$

Find the value of angles.

24) $cos\ 75°$

25) $sin\ 30°$

26) $sin(30° + 45°)$

27) $cos(-15°)$

28) $tan\ 75°$

29) $sin(-75°)$

Simplify the expressions.

30) $cos\left(\frac{\pi}{4}\right) \times cos\left(\frac{3\pi}{4}\right)$

31) $2\ sin^2(2\theta) + cos(4\theta)$

32) $sin(7x) - sin(3x)$

33) $cos(5x) + cos(x)$

Chapter 4: Answers

1) 1
2) $-\sin^3 x$
3) $\sec^3 x$
4) $\sin x$
5) $1+\sin(2x)$
6) 1
7) 1
8) $1+\sin^2 x$
9) $55°$
10) $10°$
11) $22°$
12) $17°$
13) $-\frac{1}{2}$
14) 2
15) -1
16) $-\sqrt{2}$
17) $-\frac{\sqrt{3}}{2}$
18) Undefined
19) $\frac{\sqrt{2}}{2}$
20) $\frac{\sqrt{3}}{2}$
21) $\frac{17}{25}$
22) $-\frac{24}{25}$
23) $a=\frac{\sqrt{3}}{2},\ b=\frac{\sqrt{2}-\sqrt{6}}{4}$
24) $\frac{\sqrt{6}-\sqrt{2}}{4}$
25) $\frac{1}{2}$
26) $\frac{\sqrt{6}+\sqrt{2}}{4}$
27) $\frac{\sqrt{6}+\sqrt{2}}{4}$
28) $2+\sqrt{3}$
29) $\frac{-\sqrt{6}-\sqrt{2}}{4}$
30) $-\frac{1}{2}$
31) 0
32) $2\cos(5x)\sin(2x)$
33) $2\cos(3x)\cos(2x)$

CHAPTER

5 Inverse Trigonometric Functions

Math topics that you'll learn in this chapter:

- ☑ Definition and Properties
- ☑ Arcsine, Arccosine, and Arctangent
- ☑ Applications of Inverse Trigonometric Functions

Definition and Properties

- Inverse Trigonometric Functions, also known as Arc Functions, are the inverse functions of the basic trigonometric functions. They're used to determine the angle measure given the ratio of the sides of a right triangle.
- Some properties of inverse trigonometric functions:
  - They are all functions, which means for any given input, there is exactly one output.
  - The composite of a function and its inverse always equals the identity function, e.g., $sin(asin(x)) = asin(sin(x)) = x$, for values of x in the domain of the function.
  - They are not periodic, unlike their corresponding trigonometric functions.
  - They all have limited domains and ranges due to the restrictions necessary to maintain the "function" status (as per the definition of a function where each input has exactly one unique output).
  - Their graphs are reflections of the corresponding trigonometric functions about the line $y = x$.

Example:

Consider the equation $y = sin^{-1}(x)$. Determine the range of values for y based on the definition of the inverse sine function. Suppose $x = \frac{1}{2}$. Solve for y using the inverse sine function. Now consider the function $y = cos(sin^{-1}(x))$. If $x = \frac{1}{2}$, calculate the value of y. Finally, prove the property that $cos(sin^{-1}(x)) = \sqrt{(1 - x^2)}$ for $-1 \leq x \leq 1$ by using the triangle identity theorem.

Solution: The range of values for y, when $y = sin^{-1}(x)$, is from $-\frac{\pi}{2}$ to $\frac{\pi}{2}$ (or, equivalently, from -90 degrees to 90 degrees).

If $x = \frac{1}{2}$, then $y = sin^{-1}\left(\frac{1}{2}\right)$. The sine of 30 degrees or $\frac{\pi}{6}$ radians is $\frac{1}{2}$, so $y = \frac{\pi}{6}$ (or 30 degrees) would be the solution.

For the function $y = cos(sin^{-1}(x))$, if $x = \frac{1}{2}$, then we first find $y = sin^{-1}\left(\frac{1}{2}\right)$ which is $\frac{\pi}{6}$ (as found in the previous step). The cosine of $\frac{\pi}{6}$ is $\frac{\sqrt{3}}{2}$. So, $y = \frac{\sqrt{3}}{2}$.

To prove the property that $cos(sin^{-1}(x)) = \sqrt{(1 - x^2)}$ for $-1 \leq x \leq 1$, consider a right triangle with an angle θ such that $sin(\theta) = x$. By the Pythagorean theorem, the length of the side adjacent to θ is $\sqrt{(1 - x^2)}$. Therefore, $cos(\theta) = \sqrt{(1 - x^2)}$. Since $\theta = sin^{-1}(x)$, it follows that $cos(sin^{-1}(x)) = \sqrt{(1 - x^2)}$, which completes the proof.

Arcsine, Arccosine, and Arctangent

- Arcsine, arccosine, and arctangent are inverse trigonometric functions, also known as inverse circular functions or simply as arc functions. These functions reverse the action of their respective trigonometric counterparts: *sine*, *cosine*, and *tangent*. In mathematics, they are used to determine the angle of a right-angled triangle when the lengths of two sides are known. They are denoted as $sin^{-1}(x)$, $cos^{-1}(x)$, and $tan^{-1}(x)$ or as $arcsin(x)$, $arccos(x)$, and $arctan(x)$, respectively.
    - ***Arcsine*** **($sin^{-1}(x)$ or $arcsin(x)$)**: This function is the inverse of the sine function, and it returns the angle (in radians) whose sine value is x. The domain of the arcsine function is $-1 \leq x \leq 1$, and the range is $-\frac{\pi}{2} \leq sin^{-1}(x) \leq \frac{\pi}{2}$.
    - ***Arccosine*** **($cos^{-1}(x)$ or $arccos(x)$)**: This function is the inverse of the cosine function, and it returns the angle (in radians) whose cosine value is x. The domain of the arccosine function is $-1 \leq x \leq 1$, and the range is $0 \leq cos^{-1}(x) \leq \pi$.
    - ***Arctangent*** **($tan^{-1}(x)$ or $arctan(x)$)**: This function is the inverse of the tangent function, and it returns the angle (in radians) whose tangent value is x. The domain of the arctangent function is $-\infty < x < +\infty$, and the range is $-\frac{\pi}{2} < tan^{-1}(x) < \frac{\pi}{2}$.

Examples:

Example1. Determine the value of $cos^{-1}\left(cos\frac{13\pi}{6}\right)$.

Solution: $cos^{-1}\left(cos\frac{13\pi}{6}\right) = cos^{-1}\left[cos\left(2\pi + \frac{\pi}{6}\right)\right] = cos^{-1}\left[cos\frac{\pi}{6}\right] = \frac{\pi}{6}$

Example2. Find the value of $tan^{-1}(sin\,90°)$.

Solution: $tan^{-1}(sin\,90°) = tan^{-1}(1) = 45°$ or $\frac{\pi}{4}$

Example3. What is the value of $cos^{-1}\left(sin\frac{7\pi}{6}\right)$?

Solution: $cos^{-1}\left(sin\frac{7\pi}{6}\right) = cos^{-1}\left[sin\left(\pi + \frac{\pi}{6}\right)\right] = cos^{-1}\left[-sin\frac{\pi}{6}\right] = cos^{-1}\left(-\frac{1}{2}\right) = \frac{2\pi}{3}$

Example4. What is the value of $sin^{-1}(cos\,300°)$?

Solution: $sin^{-1}(cos\,300°) = sin^{-1}(cos(360 - 60)°) = sin^{-1}\left(\frac{1}{2}\right) = 30°$

Applications of Inverse Trigonometric Functions

- Inverse trigonometric functions, also known as arc functions or cyclometric functions, are the inverses of the basic trigonometric functions like sine, cosine, and tangent. They are used to determine the angles of a triangle when the lengths or ratios of sides are known. Applications of inverse trigonometric functions are widespread in various fields, including engineering, physics, and mathematics. Key applications include:
  - **Geometry:** Inverse trigonometric functions help solve triangles and calculate angles in various geometric problems.
  - **Trigonometric Identities:** They are used to derive and prove various trigonometric identities and relationships.
  - **Calculus:** In calculus, inverse trigonometric functions are essential for solving integrals and derivatives involving trigonometric functions.
  - **Engineering:** Inverse trigonometric functions are used in various engineering fields, such as electronics, mechanics, and civil engineering, to solve problems related to waveforms, oscillations, and structural analysis.
  - **Physics:** They play a crucial role in understanding wave mechanics, analyzing oscillatory systems, and studying kinematics and dynamics.
  - **Navigation:** Inverse trigonometric functions are used in determining distances, bearings, and angles in navigation and cartography.
  - **Computer Graphics:** They help in rendering and transforming $2D$ and $3D$ models, as well as in image processing and computational geometry.

Chapter 5: Practices

Solve.

1) Consider the equation $y = arccos(x)$. Determine the domain and range of values for x and y based on the definition of the inverse cosine function. Suppose the range of values for y is $-\frac{\pi}{2} \leq y \leq \frac{\pi}{2}$. Solve for x using the inverse cosine function when $y = \frac{\pi}{4}$.

2) Consider the equation $y = arctan(x)$. Determine the domain and range of values for x and y based on the definition of the inverse tangent function. Suppose the domain of values for x is $-\infty < x < \infty$. Solve for y using the inverse tangent function when $x = \sqrt{3}$.

Find the value of each expression.

3) $cos^{-1}\left(cos\frac{2\pi}{3}\right)$

4) $tan^{-1}\left(tan\frac{3\pi}{4}\right)$

5) $tan^{-1}(sec\,\pi)$

6) $sin^{-1}\left(sin\frac{11\pi}{6}\right)$

7) $sec(cos^{-1}x)$

8) $csc\left(cos^{-1}\frac{\sqrt{3}}{2}\right)$

9) $sin^{-1}(sec\,0)$

10) $sin^{-1}\left(cot\frac{\pi}{4}\right)$

Chapter 5: Answers

1) The domain: $-1 \le x \le 1$

The range: $0 \le f(x) \le \pi$

$x = \frac{\sqrt{2}}{2}$

2) The domain: $-\infty < x < +\infty$

The range: $-\frac{\pi}{2} < f(x) < \frac{\pi}{2}$

$y = \frac{\pi}{3}$

3) $\frac{2\pi}{3}$

4) $-\frac{\pi}{4}$

5) $-\frac{\pi}{4}$

6) $-\frac{\pi}{6}$

7) $\frac{1}{x}$

8) 2

9) $\frac{\pi}{2}$

10) $\frac{\pi}{2}$

CHAPTER

6 Solving Trigonometric Equations

Math topics that you'll learn in this chapter:

☑ Basic Techniques for Solving Trigonometric Equations
☑ Factoring and Simplifying Trigonometric Expressions
☑ Solving Equations with Multiple Angles

Basic Techniques for Solving Trigonometric Equations

- Basic Techniques for Solving Trigonometric Equations involve the application of fundamental trigonometric identities and algebraic methods to find the values of the unknown variable(s) in equations that involve trigonometric functions. Key techniques include:
    - **Simplification:** Reduce the equation to its simplest form by applying trigonometric identities such as reciprocal, quotient, Pythagorean, co-function, and double-angle identities.
    - **Factoring:** Factor trigonometric expressions to simplify complex equations, which may allow them to be solved more easily.
    - **Isolating the variable:** Rearrange the equation so that the trigonometric function containing the variable is isolated on one side, making it easier to solve for the variable.
    - **Using inverse trigonometric functions:** Apply inverse trigonometric functions ($sin^{-1}, cos^{-1}, tan^{-1}$) to both sides of the equation to cancel out the trigonometric functions and obtain the value of the variable.
    - **Solving for multiple angles:** In some cases, an equation may have multiple solutions within a given range. Use the periodicity and symmetries of trigonometric functions to find all possible solutions.
    - **Graphing:** Graph the trigonometric function to visualize its behavior and obtain approximate solutions, particularly when algebraic methods prove difficult.
- By employing these techniques in combination, you can effectively solve a wide range of trigonometric equations.

Example:

Solve the trigonometric equation: $3\,sin(x) = 2\,cos^2(x)$, for x between 0 and 2π.
Solution: To solve this trigonometric equation, we can use the identity $cos^2(x) + sin^2(x) = 1$ to rewrite the equation in terms of $sin(x)$:

$$3\,sin(x) = 2\big(1 - sin^2(x)\big) \rightarrow 3\,sin(x) = 2 - 2\,sin^2(x)$$

Rearranging and factoring, we obtain: $2\,sin^2(x) + 3\,sin(x) - 2 = 0$. This is a quadratic equation in $sin(x)$, so we can solve it using the quadratic formula:
$sin(x) = \frac{-3\pm\sqrt{3^2-4(2)(-2)}}{2(2)} \rightarrow sin(x) = \frac{-3\pm\sqrt{25}}{4} \rightarrow sin(x) = \frac{1}{2}$, or $sin(x) = -2$.
The second solution is not possible since the range of $sin(x)$ is between -1 and 1, so we only consider the solution $sin(x) = \frac{1}{2}$. To find the values of x that satisfy $sin(x) = \frac{1}{2}$, so the solutions for x between 0 and 2π are: $x = \frac{\pi}{6}$ or $x = \frac{5\pi}{6}$.

Factoring and Simplifying Trigonometric Expressions

- Factoring and Simplifying Trigonometric Expressions are essential techniques in trigonometry, used to break down complex expressions and equations into simpler forms. This makes it easier to analyze, understand, and solve trigonometric problems. Key methods include:
  - **Basic Factoring:** Identify common factors in the terms of an expression and use the distributive property to factor them out.
  - **Trigonometric Identities:** Apply fundamental trigonometric identities like reciprocal, quotient, Pythagorean, co-function, and double-angle identities to simplify expressions or rewrite them in equivalent forms.
  - **Trig Functions as Algebraic Expressions:** Use substitutions to represent trigonometric functions as algebraic expressions (e.g., using $sin^2 x + cos^2 x = 1$), which can then be factored and simplified using standard algebraic techniques.
  - **Factoring Techniques:** Apply algebraic factoring techniques such as factoring by grouping, the difference of squares, and the sum/difference of cubes to simplify trigonometric expressions.
  - **Rationalizing Denominators:** Simplify expressions with trigonometric functions in the denominator by multiplying the numerator and denominator by the conjugate of the denominator, which helps eliminate complex trigonometric terms.
- By using these techniques, trigonometric expressions can be simplified, making it easier to solve related equations and understand the underlying mathematical relationships.

Example:

Factor the following trigonometric expression: $sin^2 x - sin x - 6$.
Solution: To factor the expression $sin^2 x - sin x - 6$, we can first look for two numbers that multiply to -6 and add to -1 (the coefficient of $sin x$). These numbers are -3 and 2, since $-3 \times 2 = -6$ and $-3 + 2 = -1$.
Now we can express the expression as $sin^2 x - 3 sin x + 2 sin x - 6$, and group the terms as follows: $(sin^2 x - 3 sin x) + (2 sin x - 6)$.
Next, we can factor out $sin x$ from the first group, and factor out 2 from the second group: $sin x (sin x - 3) + 2(sin x - 3)$.
Notice that we now have a common factor of $(sin x - 3)$, so we can simplify the expression as: $(sin x - 3)(sin x + 2)$.
Therefore, the factored form of $sin^2 x - sin x - 6$ is:
$(sin x - 3)(sin x + 2)$.

Solving Equations with Multiple Angles

- Solving Equations with Multiple Angles involves finding the values of the unknown variable(s) in trigonometric equations that contain multiple angles, like $2x$ or $3x$, instead of a single angle. Key techniques include:
    - **Simplification:** Use trigonometric identities, such as double-angle, half-angle, or triple-angle identities, to rewrite expressions involving multiple angles in simpler terms, making it easier to solve the equation.
    - **Substitution:** Temporarily replace the multiple-angle expression (e.g., $2x$) with a new variable (e.g., $y = 2x$) to convert the equation into a single-angle equation. Solve for the new variable, and then replace it with the original expression to find the solution(s) for the initial variable.
    - **Solve for one angle first:** If the equation contains more than one trigonometric function with different multiples of the angle (e.g., $sin(2x)$ and $cos(x)$), try to express all trigonometric functions in terms of a single angle using identities.
    - **Consider the periodicity of trigonometric functions:** Since trigonometric functions are periodic, multiple-angle equations may have multiple solutions within a given range.
- By employing these techniques, you can efficiently solve trigonometric equations involving multiple angles and find all possible solutions.

Example:

Solve the following equation for values of x between 0 and 360 degrees:

$$2\,sin(2x) + cos(x) = 0$$

Solution: We can use double-angle and sum-to-product identities to simplify the equation. First, let's rewrite the double-angle identity for sine:

$$2\,sin(2x) = 2\big(2\,sin(x)\,cos(x)\big)$$

Now, let's substitute this into the equation: $2(2\,sin(x)\,cos(x)) + cos(x) = 0$.
Expanding and rearranging the terms:

$$4\,sin(x)\,cos(x) + cos(x) = 0 \rightarrow cos(x)\,(4\,sin(x) + 1) = 0$$

Now, we have two possible cases:

$$cos(x) = 0$$
$$4\,sin(x) + 1 = 0$$

For the first case, $cos(x) = 0$, we know that $cos(x) = 0$ when $x = 90$ degrees and $x = 270$ degrees. For the second case, $4\,sin(x) + 1 = 0$, we can solve for $sin(x)$:

$$4\,sin(x) = -1 \rightarrow sin(x) = -\frac{1}{4}$$

Using the inverse sine function, we find two solutions:
$x = arcsin\left(-\frac{1}{4}\right) \approx -14.48$ degrees and $x = 180 - arcsin\left(-\frac{1}{4}\right) \approx 194.48$ degrees.

Chapter 6: Practices

Solve.

1) $3\,sin(2x) - 2\,cos(x) = 0$ for x between 0 and 2π

2) $2\,tan(2x) + 1 = 0$ in the interval $[0, 360°)$

3) $sin(x) + 2\,cos(2x) = 1$ in the interval $[0, 360°)$

Factor the expression.

4) $4\,cos^2\,\theta - 4\,cos\,\theta + 1$

5) $sin^2\,\theta + sin\,\theta - 2$

6) $cos^3\,\theta - 8\,cos\,\theta - 3\,cos^2\,\theta + 24$

7) $3\,sin^3\,x - 3\,sin^2\,x - 5\,sin\,x + 5$

Solve.

8) $5\,sin(\theta) + 3\,cos(2\theta) = 4$

9) $2\,sin(2x) - 3\,cos(x) = 0$

10) $\sqrt{cos\,x} = 2\,cos\,x - 1$

11) $2\,tan^4\,x - tan^2\,x - 15 = 0$

12) $3\,sin(\theta) + 2\,sin^2(\theta) = -1$

Chapter 6: Answers

1) $\frac{\pi}{2}, \frac{3\pi}{2}, 0.34, \pi - 0.34$

2) $76.72°, 166.72°, 256.72°, 346.72°$

3) $39.82°, 140.18°, 202.97°, 337.02°$

4) $(2\cos\theta - 1)^2$

5) $(\sin\theta - 1)(\sin\theta + 2)$

6) $(\cos\theta - 3)(\cos^2\theta - 8)$

7) $(\sin x - 1)(3\sin^2 x - 5)$

8) $30°, 19.47°, 160.52°, 150°$

9) $90°, 270°, 48.59°, 131.41°$

10) $0°$

11) $60°, 120°$

12) $210°, 330°, 270°$

CHAPTER

7 Oblique Triangles and the Law of Sines

Math topics that you'll learn in this chapter:

- ☑ Non-Right Triangles
- ☑ The Law of Sines
- ☑ Ambiguous Case (SSA)
- ☑ Applications of the Law of Sines

Non-Right Triangles

- Non-right triangles in trigonometry refer to triangles that do not have a 90-degree angle. In these triangles, the sides and angles still have relationships with each other, but these relationships are slightly more complex than in right triangles.
- There are two primary laws used in dealing with non-right triangles: the Law of Sines and the Law of Cosines.
  - The Law of Sines states that the ratio of the length of a side of a triangle to the sine of the angle opposite that side is the same for all sides and angles in a given triangle. In mathematical terms, for a triangle with sides of lengths a, b, c and angles A, B, C opposite those sides respectively, the law is expressed as:
  $$\frac{a}{\sin A} = \frac{b}{\sin B} = \frac{c}{\sin C}$$
  - The Law of Cosines, which is a generalization of the Pythagorean theorem, states that for a triangle with sides of lengths a, b, c and an angle C opposite side c, the following relationship holds:
  $$c^2 = a^2 + b^2 - 2ab \times \cos C$$

Example:

In triangle ABC, angle A measures 35 degrees, side a has a length of 10 cm, and side b has a length of 8 cm. Use the Law of Sines to find the measure of angle B.
Solution: To find the measure of angle B in triangle ABC, we can use the Law of Sines. In this case, angle A measures 35 degrees, side a has a length of 10 cm, and side b has a length of 8 cm. Let's substitute the given values into the Law of Sines:

$$\frac{10}{sin(35°)} = \frac{8}{sin(B)} = \frac{c}{sin(C)}$$

First, let's find the measure of angle B:

$$\frac{10}{sin(35°)} = \frac{8}{sin(B)} \rightarrow 10 \times sin(B) = 8 \times sin(35°) \rightarrow sin(B) = \frac{8 \times sin(35°)}{10}$$

$sin(B) \approx 0.459$

Now, let's find the measure of angle B by taking the inverse sine ($arcsin$) of the value: $B \approx arcsin(0.459) \rightarrow B \approx 27.32$ degrees.

The Law of Sines

- When you know the measures of 2 factors in a triangle as well as one of the sides, as in the case of ASA or AAS, you can use the law of sines to determine the measures of the other two angles and the other side.
- For ΔABC, the Law of Sines states the following:

$$\frac{a}{\sin A} = \frac{b}{\sin B} = \frac{c}{\sin C}$$

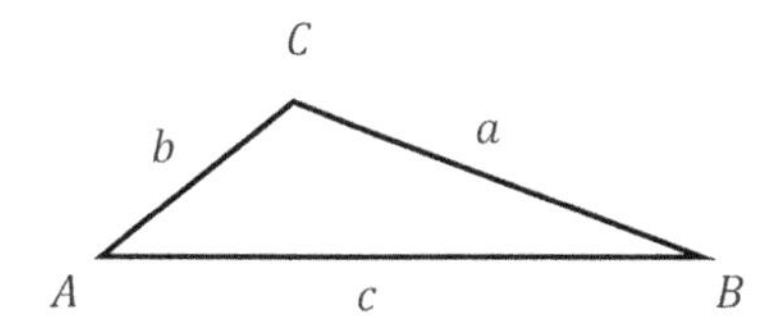

Examples:

Example 1. For a triangle, it is given $a = 12\ cm$, $c = 14.5\ cm$ and angle $C = 54°$. Find the angle A of the triangle.

Solution: Use the Law of Sines to find the angle A.

$$\frac{a}{\sin A} = \frac{c}{\sin C}$$

$$\frac{12}{\sin A} = \frac{14.5}{\sin 54°} \rightarrow \sin A = \frac{12 \times \sin 54°}{14.5}$$

$$\sin A = \frac{12 \times 0.8}{14.5} = \frac{9.6}{14.5} = 0.66 \rightarrow A = 42.03°$$

Example 2. In the ABC triangle, find side a.

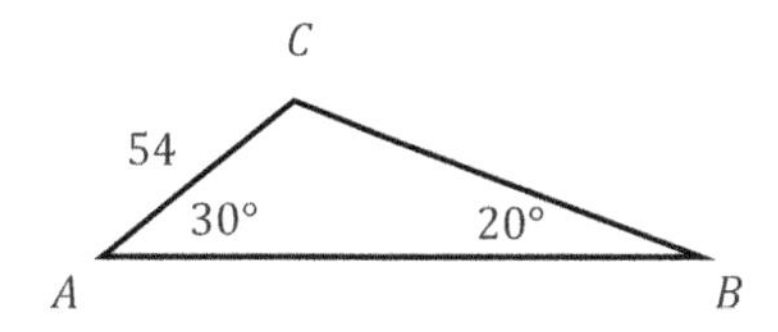

Solution: Use the Law of Sines to find side a.

$$\frac{a}{\sin 30°} = \frac{54}{\sin 20°} \rightarrow a = \frac{54 \times \sin 30°}{\sin 20°}$$

$$a = \frac{54 \times 0.5}{0.34} = \frac{27}{0.34} = 79.41$$

Example 3. For a triangle, it is given $A = 62°$, $B = 55°$ and $c = 5\ cm$. Find side b of the triangle.

Solution: Use the Law of Sines to find side b.

$$62° + 55° + C = 180° \rightarrow C = 63°$$

$$\frac{b}{\sin B} = \frac{c}{\sin C} \rightarrow \frac{b}{\sin 55°} = \frac{5}{\sin 63°} \rightarrow b = \frac{\sin 55° \times 5}{\sin 63°} \rightarrow b = 4.59\ cm$$

Ambiguous Case (SSA)

- The Ambiguous Case, also known as the Side-Side-Angle (SSA) case, is a concept in trigonometry that refers to a situation where two triangles can potentially have the same given information, specifically two sides and a non-included angle. This can result in multiple possible solutions when trying to solve for the unknown values of a triangle.
- The ambiguous case arises when you are given two sides (a and b) and an angle (A) opposite one of the sides (a), but you don't know the relationship between the angle and the other side (b). Depending on the length of the sides and the size of the angle, there may be one, two, or no solutions for the triangle:
  - One solution: If side (a) is longer than the altitude of the triangle from angle A, there is only one possible triangle.
  - Two solutions: If side (a) is shorter than the altitude but longer than side b, there will be two possible triangles.
  - No solution: If side (a) is shorter than side b and the angle A is acute, there is no possible triangle.
- The Ambiguous Case is important in trigonometry as it highlights the need to consider multiple possibilities when solving problems involving triangles with given side-side-angle information.

Example:

Triangle ABC has side lengths $AB = 12\ cm$, $BC = 6\ cm$, and angle $A = 45$ degrees. Determine whether it is possible to construct triangle ABC, and if so, find the possible measures of angles B and C.

Solution: To determine if it is possible to construct a triangle ABC, we can use the law of sines. The law of sines states that for any triangle with sides a, b, and c, and angles A, B, and C opposite those respective sides: $\frac{a}{\sin A} = \frac{b}{\sin B} = \frac{c}{\sin C}$.

In this case, we have side $AB = 12\ cm$, side $BC = 6\ cm$, and angle $A = 45$ degrees.

Let's use the law of sines to solve for the remaining angles:

$$\frac{6}{sin(45)} = \frac{12}{sin(C)} \rightarrow sin(C) = \frac{12 \times sin(45)}{6} \rightarrow sin(C) = 1.41$$

Since the sine of an angle cannot be greater than 1, it is not possible to have a triangle with the given side lengths and angle measures. Therefore, it is not possible to construct triangle ABC with the given measurements.

Applications of the Law of Sines

- The Law of Sines is a fundamental trigonometric principle used to solve various problems in mathematics, particularly in the realm of geometry. It states that in any triangle, the ratio of the length of a side to the sine of its opposite angle is constant for all three sides. Mathematically, it is expressed as:

$$\frac{a}{sin(A)} = \frac{b}{sin(B)} = \frac{c}{sin(C)}$$

- Where a, b, and c represent the side lengths and A, B, and C represent the opposite angles of a triangle.
- In mathematics, the Law of Sines is applied in several ways:
  - **Solving triangles:** The Law of Sines is particularly useful in solving non-right triangles, allowing for the determination of unknown side lengths and angles when given specific information about the triangle, such as side-angle-side (SAS) or angle-side-angle (ASA) configurations.
  - **Area of a triangle:** The Law of Sines can be employed to calculate the area of a triangle when given two sides and the included angle. The formula for this application is: $Area = \left(\frac{1}{2}\right) ab \times sin(C)$, where a and b are the given side lengths and C is the included angle.
  - **Ambiguous case (SSA):** When given two side lengths and a non-included angle in a triangle, the Law of Sines can be used to determine if the triangle is unique, has two possible solutions, or has no valid solution.
  - **Spherical geometry:** In spherical geometry, the Law of Sines is adapted for solving problems involving spherical triangles, which are crucial in navigation, astronomy, and geodesy.
  - **Analytic geometry:** The Law of Sines is applied in coordinate systems to determine the distance between two points, the angle between two lines, or the area of a polygon.
- These examples illustrate the diverse applications of the Law of Sines in mathematics, making it an indispensable tool in the study and understanding of various mathematical concepts and problems.

bit.ly/3rVyzOn

Chapter 7: Practices

Solve.

1) Triangle ABC is a non-right triangle with side lengths $AB = 10\ cm$, $BC = 12\ cm$. Angle BAC measures 60 degrees. Calculate the measures of angles ABC.

2) In a non-right triangle ABC, where angle A is acute and angle B is obtuse, the lengths of the sides are given as follows: side $AB = 8\ cm$, side $BC = 10\ cm$, and side $AC = 12\ cm$. Find the measures of angles A.

Find each measurement indicated. Round your answers to the nearest tenth.

3) ________

B
36.9°
15
12
53.1°
A
x
C

4) ________

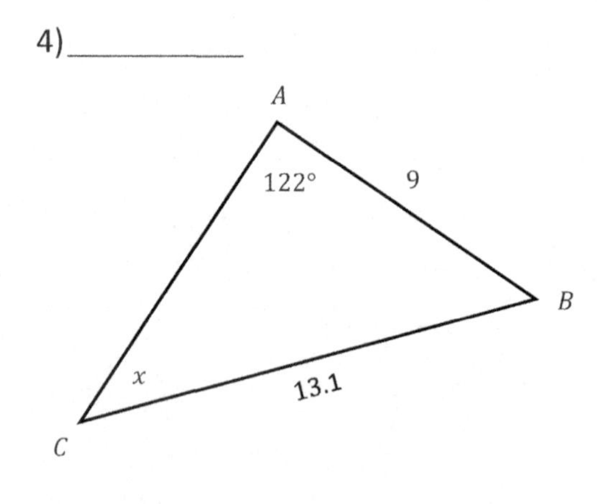

5) $m\angle C = 14°$, $m\angle A = 24°$, $c = 9$ ________

6) $m\angle C = 125°$, $b = 8$, $c = 24$ ________

Solve.

7) Triangle XYZ has side lengths $XY = 10\ cm$, $YZ = 5\ cm$, and angle $X = 30$ degrees. Determine whether it is possible to construct a triangle XYZ, and if so, find the possible measures of angles Y and Z.

Chapter 7: Answers

1) $73.81°$
2) $55.77°$
3) 9
4) $35.64°$
5) $m\angle B = 142°$, $a = 15.1$, $b = 22.9$
6) $m\angle A = 39.2°$, $m\angle B = 15.8°$, $a = 18.5$
7) $Z = 14.48°$ and $Y = 135.52°$

CHAPTER

8 The Law of Cosines

Math topics that you'll learn in this chapter:

- ☑ Derivation of the Law of Cosines
- ☑ Solving Triangles with the Law of Cosines
- ☑ Applications of the Law of Cosines

Derivation of the Law of Cosines

- The Law of Cosines states: $c^2 = a^2 + b^2 - 2ab \times cos(C)$
  Where: a, b, and c are the lengths of the sides of a triangle.
  C is the angle opposite side c.
- Here's a derivation of the Law of Cosines using the dot product concept from vector algebra:
  - Consider a non-right triangle with sides a, b, and c, with C being the angle between sides a and b. To derive the law of cosines, first, draw a line from the angle C perpendicular to side c, forming two right triangles. This line divides side c into two segments: one with length x and the other with length $(c - x)$.

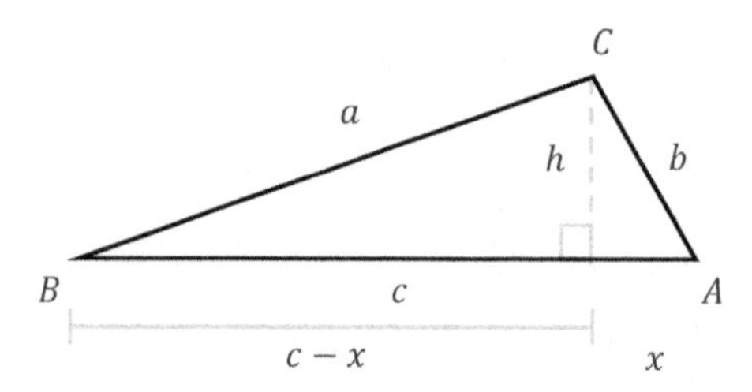

  - By the Pythagorean theorem, the length of the line drawn (h) can be determined in terms of a, b, and x: $h^2 = b^2 - x^2$ and $h^2 = a^2 - (c - x)^2$.
  - By equating and simplifying these equations, we get:

$$a^2 - (c - x)^2 = b^2 - x^2 \rightarrow a^2 - (c^2 - 2cx + x^2) = b^2 - x^2$$

  - This simplifies to: $a^2 - b^2 = c^2 - 2cx$.
  - We know that $cos(A) = \frac{x}{b}$ from one of the right triangles. Solving for x gives us $x = b \times cos(A)$. Substitute this into the previous equation:

$$a^2 - b^2 = c^2 - 2c \times b \times cos(A)$$

  - Rearranging terms, we get the law of cosines:

$$a^2 = b^2 + c^2 - 2b \times c \times cos(A)$$

Solving Triangles with the Law of Cosines

- Solving a triangle using the Law of Cosines involves finding all unknown sides and angles of the triangle. This law is often used when we know:
  - All three sides, but no angles (SSS scenario).
  - Two sides and their included angle (SAS scenario).
- The Law of Cosines is formulated as $c^2 = a^2 + b^2 - 2ab \times cos(C)$.
- For SSS, you can find one angle (say, C) using this rearranged formula:

$$C = arccos\left[\frac{a^2 + b^2 - c^2}{2ab}\right]$$

- For the second angle (say, A), use the formula: $A = arccos\left[\frac{b^2+c^2-a^2}{2bc}\right]$.
- The third angle, B, is found by knowing that the sum of angles in a triangle is 180 degrees.
- For SAS, use the Law of Cosines to find the unknown side, and then use it again or use the Law of Sines to find the remaining angles. Always remember to convert between radians and degrees if necessary, depending on your calculation or programming context.

Example:

Find angle B in the ABC triangle.

Solution: Use the Law of Cosines to find angle B.

$$cos\,B = \frac{a^2 + c^2 - b^2}{2ac}$$

$$cos\,B = \frac{8^2 + 10^2 - 14^2}{2 \times 8 \times 10} = \frac{64 + 100 - 196}{160} = -0.2$$

$B = 101.54°$

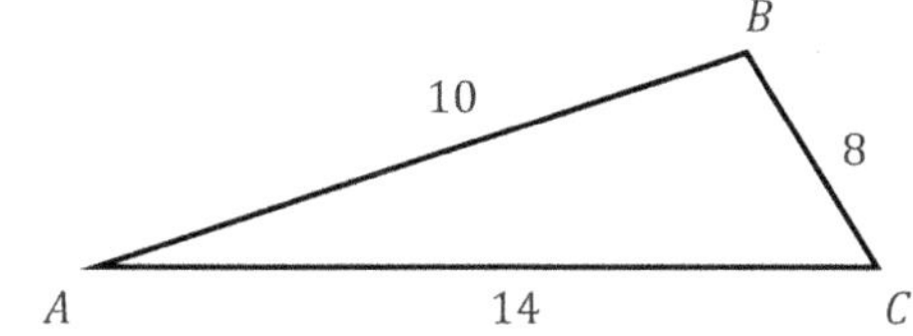

Applications of the Law of Cosines

- The Law of Cosines is applicable in various fields and has numerous applications, some of which are listed below:
  - **Solving triangles:** The Law of Cosines is used to solve oblique triangles, i.e., triangles that do not have a right angle. Given any three pieces of information (sides or angles), one can use the Law of Cosines along with other trigonometric rules to solve for the remaining sides and angles.
  - **Distance calculation:** In navigation, geography, and surveying, the Law of Cosines can help determine the distance between two points on the Earth's surface. By considering the Earth as a sphere, one can use spherical trigonometry and the Law of Cosines to estimate the great-circle distance (shortest distance) between two points.
  - **Vector analysis:** In physics and engineering, the Law of Cosines is used to find the magnitude and direction of a resultant vector when two or more vectors are acting together. This is especially helpful when dealing with forces, velocities, or displacements in two or three dimensions.
  - **Geodesy and cartography:** The Law of Cosines is widely used in geodesy and cartography to accurately represent and measure the Earth's surface. It helps to calculate distances, angles, and areas on maps and aids in the creation of map projections.
  - **Engineering and architecture:** In structural analysis, the Law of Cosines is used to calculate forces and stresses acting on various components of a structure. It is also utilized in the design and analysis of various mechanical systems, such as gears and linkages.
  - **Astronomy:** The Law of Cosines plays a vital role in calculating the position of celestial bodies and their movements. It helps astronomers determine the angular separation between two celestial objects, which in turn aids in the calculation of their actual distances and positions.
  - **Computer graphics:** In computer graphics and gaming, the Law of Cosines is employed in various algorithms for rendering and simulating $3D$ environments. It is also used in the calculation of shading and lighting effects to create realistic images and animations.
- These are just a few examples of the many applications of the Law of Cosines in various fields. It remains a fundamental concept in mathematics and science, helping us to understand and solve complex problems in diverse areas.

Chapter 8: Practices

Find each measurement indicated. Round your answers to the nearest tenth.

1) ________

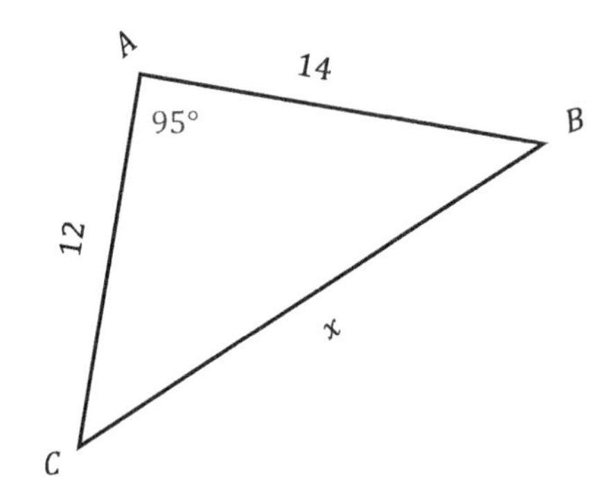

2) ________

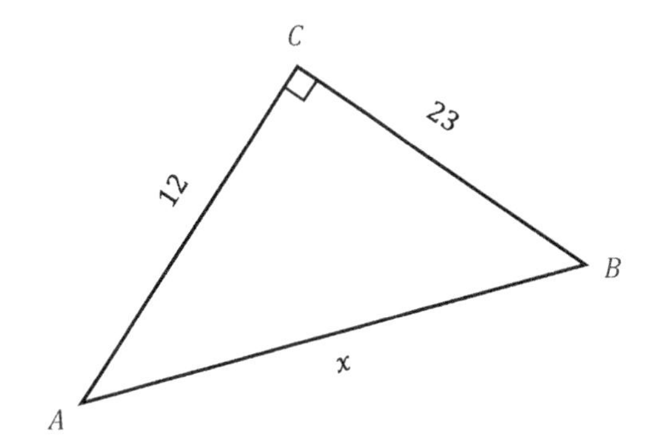

3) In ΔABC, $a = 15\ cm$, $b = 10\ cm$, $c = 7\ cm$

____

4) In ΔABC, $a = 18\ cm$, $b = 15\ cm$, $c = 11\ cm$

____

5) In ΔABC, $a = 12\ cm$, $b = 8\ cm$, $c = 10\ cm$

____

6) In ΔABC, $a = 12\ cm$, $m\angle B = 42°$, $c = 15\ cm$

____

Chapter 8: Answers

1) 19.2

2) 25.9

3) $m\angle A = 122.9°$, $m\angle B = 34°$, $m\angle C = 23.1°$

4) $m\angle A = 86.1°$, $m\angle B = 56.3°$, $m\angle C = 37.6°$

5) $m\angle A = 82.8°$, $m\angle B = 41.4°$, $m\angle C = 55.8°$

6) $m\angle A = 52.9°$, $m\angle C = 85.1°$, $b = 10\ cm$

CHAPTER

9 Trigonometric Form of Complex Numbers

Math topics that you'll learn in this chapter:

- ☑ Complex Numbers in Trigonometric Form
- ☑ Multiplication and Division of Complex Numbers
- ☑ Powers and Roots of Complex Numbers

Complex Numbers in Trigonometric Form

- Complex numbers in trigonometric form, also known as polar form, is a way to represent complex numbers using the magnitude (r) and the angle (θ) instead of the traditional Cartesian form, which uses real and imaginary components $(a + bi)$. This representation is particularly useful in solving problems involving multiplication, division, and powers of complex numbers, as it simplifies the calculations.
- A complex number in trigonometric form is represented as:

$$z = r\big(cos(\theta) + i \times sin(\theta)\big)$$

- Where z is the complex number, r is the magnitude (also called the modulus) of the complex number, θ is the angle (also called the argument or phase) measured in radians, and i is the imaginary unit $(i^2 = -1)$.
- To convert a complex number from Cartesian form to trigonometric form, the following formulas are used:

$$r = \sqrt{a^2 + b^2},\ \theta = arctan\frac{b}{a}$$

- Conversely, to convert a complex number from trigonometric form to Cartesian form, use:

$$a = r\,cos(\theta),\ b = r\,sin(\theta)$$

- The trigonometric form is particularly useful when performing operations like multiplication and division of complex numbers, as well as when calculating powers and roots, as these operations become much simpler when dealing with magnitudes and angles.

Example:

Find the trigonometric form of the complex number $8 + 6i$, where $0 < \theta < \pi$.

Solution: We need to determine its magnitude (r) and argument (θ).

The magnitude (r) of a complex number $z = a + bi$ is given by the formula:

$$r = \sqrt{a^2 + b^2}$$

In this case, $a = 8$ and $b = 6$, so we have: $r = \sqrt{6^2 + 8^2} = 10$.

The argument (θ) of a complex number can be determined using the *arctan* function: $\theta = arctan\frac{b}{a} \to \theta = arctan\left(\frac{6}{8}\right) = arctan(0.75) \approx 0.6435$ in radians

Since the given condition is $0 < \theta < \pi$, the calculated argument is already within the desired range.

$$z = 10\big(cos(0.6435) + i\,sin(0.6435)\big)$$

Multiplication and Division of Complex Numbers

- Multiplication and division of complex numbers in trigonometric form is a streamlined process that involves manipulating the magnitudes and angles of the numbers involved. This representation simplifies these operations compared to using the Cartesian form.
- Given two complex numbers in the trigonometric form:

$$z_1 = r_1\big(cos(\theta_1) + i\,sin(\theta_1)\big)$$
$$z_2 = r_2\big(cos(\theta_2) + i\,sin(\theta_2)\big)$$

1) Multiplication:

- To multiply z_1 and z_2, multiply their magnitudes and add their angles:

$$z_1 \times z_2 = (r_1 \times r_2)\big(cos(\theta_1 + \theta_2) + i \times sin(\theta_1 + \theta_2)\big)$$

2) Division:

- To divide z_1 by z_2, divide their magnitudes and subtract their angles:

$$\frac{z_1}{z_2} = \left(\frac{r_1}{r_2}\right)(cos(\theta_1 - \theta_2) + i \times sin(\theta_1 - \theta_2))$$

- These formulas make multiplication and division of complex numbers in a trigonometric form much simpler than in Cartesian form, as they require fewer calculations and avoid dealing with the imaginary unit (i) directly.

Example:

Given the complex numbers z_1 and z_2 in trigonometric form, find the product and quotient of the two numbers. Let $z_1 = 4\big(cos(30°) + i\,sin(30°)\big)$ and $z_2 = 5\big(cos(150°) + i\,sin(150°)\big)$. Find: $z_1 \times z_2$, $\frac{z_1}{z_2}$.

Solution: To find the product and quotient of two complex numbers in trigonometric form, we follow these steps:

Multiply (or divide) their magnitudes. Add (or subtract) their angles.

Given $z_1 = 4\big(cos(30°) + i\,sin(30°)\big)$ and $z_2 = 5\big(cos(150°) + i\,sin(150°)\big)$:

Product: $z_1 \times z_2$. Magnitude: $4 \times 5 = 20$. Angle: $30° + 150° = 180°$.

$$z_1 \times z_2 = 20\big(cos(180°) + i \times sin(180°)\big)$$

Quotient: $\frac{z_1}{z_2}$. Magnitude: $\frac{4}{5} = 0.8$. Angle: $30° - 150° = -120°$.

Finally, $\frac{z_1}{z_2} = 0.8\big(cos(-120°) + i \times sin(-120°)\big)$, then:

$$\frac{z_1}{z_2} = 0.8(cos(240°) + i \times sin(240°))$$

Powers and Roots of Complex Numbers

- **Powers of Complex Numbers:** De Moivre's theorem is typically used to find the power of a complex number in trigonometric form. The theorem states that for any integer n:

$$[r(\cos\theta + i\sin\theta)]^n = r^n(\cos(n\theta) + i\sin(n\theta))$$

- So, to find the nth power of a complex number, you raise r to the nth power and multiply the angle θ by n.
- **Roots of Complex Numbers:** The nth root of a complex number in trigonometric form can be found by taking the nth root of r and dividing the angle θ by n. However, there's a catch: because of the periodic nature of trigonometric functions, there are n different complex numbers that are nth roots of a given complex number. These roots are evenly spaced around the unit circle in the complex plane.
- If $z = r(\cos\theta + i\sin\theta)$, the nth roots of z are given by:

$$z_k = r^{\frac{1}{n}}\left[\cos\left(\frac{\theta+2\pi k}{n}\right) + i\sin\left(\frac{\theta+2\pi k}{n}\right)\right], \text{ for } k = 0, 1, \cdots, n-1.$$

- This formula gives n roots, including z itself.
- In summary, the trigonometric form of complex numbers simplifies the process of finding powers and roots of complex numbers, thanks to De Moivre's theorem and the cyclical properties of trigonometric functions.

Example:

Find the fourth power of the complex number $z = 3\left(\cos\frac{\pi}{6} + i\sin\frac{\pi}{6}\right)$ in trigonometric form.

Solution: In this case, we have $z = 3\left(\cos\frac{\pi}{6} + i\sin\frac{\pi}{6}\right)$, so the magnitude r is 3, and the angle θ is $\frac{\pi}{6}$. We want to find z^4. Using De Moivre's theorem, we have:

$z^4 = \left[3\left(\cos\frac{\pi}{6} + i\sin\frac{\pi}{6}\right)\right]^4$

First, let's raise the magnitude to the power of 4: $r^4 = 3^4 = 81$.

Next, we multiply the angle by 4: $\theta \times 4 = \left(\frac{\pi}{6}\right) \times 4 = \frac{\pi}{6} + \frac{\pi}{6} + \frac{\pi}{6} + \frac{\pi}{6} = \frac{4\pi}{6} = \frac{2\pi}{3}$.

Now, we have the magnitude and the angle for z^4: $z^4 = 81\left(\cos\left(\frac{2\pi}{3}\right) + i\sin\left(\frac{2\pi}{3}\right)\right)$.

Chapter 9: Practices

Find the trigonometric form of the following complex numbers.

1) $5 - 12i$
2) $24 - 7i$
3) $3 + 4i$
4) $21 + 20i$

Solve.

5) Given the complex numbers z_1 and z_2 in trigonometric form, determine the product and quotient of the two numbers. Let $z_1 = 3(cos(45°) + i\,sin(45°))$ and $z_2 = 2(cos(120°) + i\,sin(120°))$.
Calculate: $z_1 \times z_2$ and $z_1 \div z_2$.
6) Given the complex numbers z_1 and z_2 in trigonometric form, determine the product and quotient of the two numbers. Let $z_1 = 2(cos(60°) + i\,sin(60°))$ and $z_2 = 3(cos(210°) + i\,sin(210°))$.
Calculate: $z_1 \times z_2$ and $z_1 \div z_2$.
7) Given the complex numbers z_1 and z_2 in trigonometric form, determine the product and quotient of the two numbers. Let $z_1 = 8(cos(200°) + i\,sin(200°))$ and $z_2 = 2(cos(110°) + i\,sin(110°))$.
Calculate: $z_1 \times z_2$ and $z_1 \div z_2$.
8) Given the complex numbers z_1 and z_2 in trigonometric form, determine the product and quotient of the two numbers. Let $z_1 = 9(cos(90°) + i\,sin(90°))$ and $z_2 = 5(cos(40°) + i\,sin(40°))$.
Calculate: $z_1 \times z_2$ and $z_1 \div z_2$.

Write the answer in the trigonometric form of the complex number.

9) $z = 2\left(cos\left(\frac{\pi}{3}\right) + i\,sin\left(\frac{\pi}{3}\right)\right) \rightarrow z^6 = ?$
10) $z = 5\left(cos\left(\frac{4\pi}{5}\right) + i\,sin\left(\frac{4\pi}{5}\right)\right) \rightarrow z^3 = ?$
11) $z = 512\left(cos\left(\frac{\pi}{4}\right) + i\,sin\left(\frac{\pi}{4}\right)\right) \rightarrow \sqrt[3]{z} = ?$
12) $z = 81\left(cos\left(\frac{\pi}{3}\right) + i\,sin\left(\frac{\pi}{3}\right)\right) \rightarrow \sqrt[4]{z} = ?$

Chapter 9: Answers

1) $13(cos(-1.18) + i\,sin(-1.18))$

2) $25(cos(-0.28) + i\,sin(-0.28))$

3) $5(cos(0.93) + i\,sin(0.93))$

4) $29(cos(0.76) + i\,sin(0.76))$

5) $z_1 \times z_1 = 6[cos(165°) + i\,sin(165°)]$

   $z_1 \div z_1 = \left(\frac{3}{2}\right)[cos(-75°) + i\,sin(-75°)]$

6) $z_1 \times z_1 = 6[cos(270°) + i\,sin(270°)]$

   $z_1 \div z_1 = \left(\frac{2}{3}\right)[cos(-150°) + i\,sin(-150°)]$

7) $z_1 \times z_1 = 16[cos(310°) + i\,sin(310°)]$

   $z_1 \div z_1 = 4[cos(90°) + i\,sin(90°)]$

8) $z_1 \times z_1 = 45[cos(130°) + i\,sin(130°)]$

   $z_1 \div z_1 = \left(\frac{9}{5}\right)[cos(50°) + i\,sin(50°)]$

9) 64

10) $125\left(cos\left(\frac{2\pi}{5}\right) + i\,sin\left(\frac{2\pi}{5}\right)\right)$

11) $8\left(cos\left(\frac{\pi}{12}\right) + i\,sin\left(\frac{\pi}{12}\right)\right)$

12) $3\left(cos\left(\frac{\pi}{12}\right) + i\,sin\left(\frac{\pi}{12}\right)\right)$

CHAPTER

10 Polar Coordinates and Graphs

Math topics that you'll learn in this chapter:

- ☑ Introduction to Polar Coordinates
- ☑ Converting Between Polar and Rectangular Coordinates
- ☑ Graphing Polar Equations
- ☑ Applications of Polar Coordinates

Introduction to Polar Coordinates

- Polar coordinates are a two-dimensional coordinate system, just like the Cartesian (or rectangular) coordinate system. However, instead of using horizontal and vertical displacements (x and y) to locate points, polar coordinates locate points in the plane using a distance and an angle.
- The polar coordinate system is particularly useful in situations where the problem has rotational symmetry, for example in the study of circular and elliptical paths in physics and engineering.
- Here's a breakdown of polar coordinates:
  - **Radius (r):** The first element of a polar coordinate is 'r', which represents the direct distance from the origin (O) to the point in the plane. The value of 'r' can be any non-negative real number.
  - **Theta (θ):** The second element of a polar coordinate is 'θ', an angle measured counterclockwise from the positive x −axis to the line segment that joins the point to the origin.
- For example, the polar coordinates $(r, \theta) = \left(3, \frac{\pi}{2}\right)$ represent the point that is 3 units away from the origin, in the direction $\frac{\pi}{2}$ radians (or 90 degrees) counterclockwise from the positive x −axis. This point would be at (0,3) in Cartesian coordinates.

Example:

Find the angle, in degrees, between the positive x −axis and the line segment connecting the origin to the point $(3, 4)$ in the polar coordinate system.

Solution: To find the angle between the positive x −axis and the line segment connecting the origin to the point (3,4) in the polar coordinate system, we can use the angular coordinate (θ) of the point.

The angular coordinate (θ) represents the angle measured counterclockwise from the positive x −axis to the line segment connecting the origin to the point. In this case, θ can be found using the tangent function:

$$\theta = arctan\left(\frac{y}{x}\right) = arctan\left(\frac{4}{3}\right)$$

Using a calculator, we can find that $arctan\left(\frac{4}{3}\right)$ is approximately 53.13°.

Therefore, the angle between the positive x −axis and the line segment connecting the origin to the point (3,4) is approximately 53.13°.

Converting Between Polar and Rectangular Coordinates

Rectangular to Polar Conversion:

- Given a point in rectangular coordinates (x, y), we can find the polar coordinates (r, θ) using the following equations:
  - The radial coordinate 'r' is found using the Pythagorean theorem:
    $$r = \sqrt{x^2 + y^2}$$
  - The angular coordinate 'θ' can be found using trigonometric functions. The tangent of 'θ' is $\frac{y}{x}$, so $\theta = arctan\left(\frac{y}{x}\right)$. However, the value of 'θ' must be adjusted based on the quadrant of the point:
    - ❖ Quadrant I: $\theta = arctan\left(\frac{y}{x}\right)$
    - ❖ Quadrant II: $\theta = \pi + arctan\left(\frac{y}{x}\right)$
    - ❖ Quadrant III: $\theta = \pi + arctan\left(\frac{y}{x}\right)$
    - ❖ Quadrant IV: $\theta = 2\pi + arctan\left(\frac{y}{x}\right)$

Polar to Rectangular Conversion:

- Given a point in polar coordinates (r, θ), we can find the rectangular coordinates (x, y) using the following equations:
  - The x −coordinate can be found using the formula: $x = r \times cos(\theta)$.
  - The y −coordinate can be found using the formula: $y = r \times sin(\theta)$.
- Note: Make sure that the angle θ is in the correct form (usually radians) for the trigonometric functions.
- Remember, these conversion methods are applicable in a $2D$ plane. If you are working with $3D$ space, you would use cylindrical or spherical coordinates instead of polar.

Example:

Sarah is located at coordinates $(1, \sqrt{3})$ in the rectangular coordinate system. Convert Sarah's coordinates to polar coordinates.

Solution: To convert Sarah's coordinates $(1, \sqrt{3})$ from rectangular to polar coordinates, we can use the following formulas: $\mathrm{r} = \sqrt{(x^2 + y^2)}$, $\theta = arctan\left(\frac{y}{x}\right)$.

Plugging in the values for Sarah's coordinates, we have:

$r = \sqrt{1^2 + (\sqrt{3})^2} = \sqrt{1 + 3} = \sqrt{4} = 2$, and $\theta = arctan\left(\frac{\sqrt{3}}{1}\right) = arctan(\sqrt{3}) = \frac{\pi}{3}$.

Therefore, Sarah's coordinates in the polar form are approximately $\left(2, \frac{\pi}{3}\right)$.

Graphing Polar Equations

- Graphing polar equations involves plotting points that satisfy the equation on a polar coordinate plane, which uses radial and angular coordinates instead of the conventional Cartesian coordinates.
- Here's a brief step-by-step process:
  - **Understand the Polar Coordinate System:** This system is defined by a distance (r) from a central point (the origin) and an angle (θ) from the positive x −axis.
  - **Identify the Polar Equation:** Polar equations can take various forms, such as circles, spirals, or roses.
  - **Create a Table of Values:** Substitute various values of θ into the equation and solve for r to understand what points satisfy the equation.
  - **Plot Points:** Plot these (r, θ) values on your polar graph. The angle θ is counterclockwise from the x −axis, and r is the distance from the origin.
  - **Connect the Dots:** Draw a smooth curve that connects these plotted points to form the graph of the polar equation.
  - **Analyze the Graph:** Identify the graph's properties, such as symmetry or intercepts, and determine the maximum and minimum values.

Example:

Consider the polar equation $r = 4 + 2\,cos(\theta)$. Sketch the graph of the polar equation on the coordinate plane.

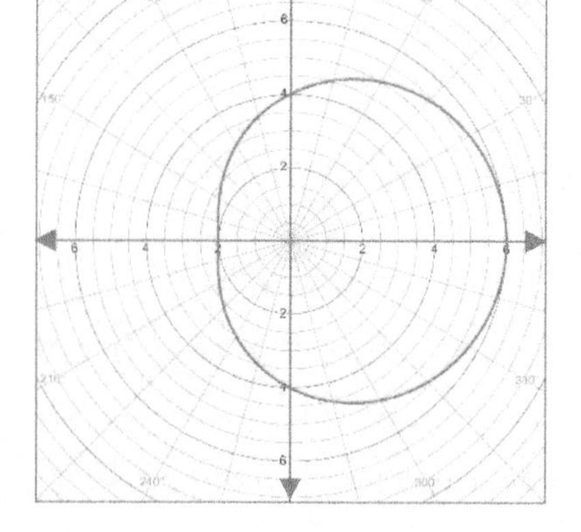

Solution: To sketch the graph, we can plot points for different values of θ and corresponding values of r:

When $\theta = 0°$, $r = 6$. Plot a point at $(6, 0)$.

When $\theta = 45°$,

$r = 4 + 2\,cos(45°) = 4 + 2\left(\frac{\sqrt{2}}{2}\right) = 4 + \sqrt{2} \approx 5.41$.

Plot a point at $(5.41, 45°)$.

When $\theta = 90°$, $r = 4$. Plot a point at $(4, 90°)$.

When $\theta = 135°$, $r = 4 + 2\,cos(135°) = 4 + 2\left(-\frac{\sqrt{2}}{2}\right) = 4 - \sqrt{2} \approx 2.59$. Plot a point at $(2.59, 135°)$.

When $\theta = 180°$, $r = 2$. Plot a point at $(2, 180°)$.

Continue this process until you complete the full 360° rotation.

Once all the points are plotted, connect them smoothly to form the graph of the polar equation $r = 4 + 2\,cos(\theta)$.

Applications of Polar Coordinates

- Polar coordinates are used extensively in various fields of mathematics, physics, engineering, computer science, and more. Here are some specific applications:
  - **Physics and Engineering:** Polar coordinates are often used in physics and engineering to describe phenomena that have a clear point of origin or center. For example, in mechanics, polar coordinates are used to analyze circular motion, oscillatory motion, and wave phenomena. In electrical engineering, they are used in signal processing and system analysis (especially in the frequency domain using the Fourier Transform).
  - **Astronomy:** Astronomers use polar coordinates to describe the location of stars and other celestial bodies. By using the observer as the origin point, the angle from a reference direction (like due north) and the distance to the star can be used to pinpoint its location.
  - **Computer Graphics and Game Design:** Polar coordinates are used in computer graphics and game design, especially for objects that move or exist in a circular pattern. For example, polar coordinates can be used to rotate an object around a point or to create circular paths for objects to follow.
  - **Robotics:** In robotics, polar coordinates are used in the design of robotic arms and other machinery. The polar coordinate system makes it easier to calculate and control the movement of these machines.
  - **Geographic Information Systems (GIS):** Polar coordinates are used in geographic information systems to describe locations on the earth's surface. This is especially useful in navigation and cartography.
  - **Mathematics:** In calculus, polar coordinates can be used to solve certain types of integrals and differential equations more easily than with Cartesian coordinates. Also, in complex analysis, complex numbers are often represented in a polar form.
  - **Meteorology:** Polar coordinates are used in meteorology to represent wind direction and speed. The angle represents the wind direction, and the radial distance represents the speed.
- These are just a few examples of how polar coordinates are applied in various fields. In general, any situation where a phenomenon is naturally centered around a point or naturally moves in a circular or spherical pattern is a candidate for the use of polar coordinates.

Chapter 10: Practices

Solve.

1) Find the distance between the origin and the point $\left(5, \frac{\pi}{3}\right)$ in the polar coordinate system.
2) A satellite is orbiting the Earth in a polar orbit with a radius of 1000 kilometers. Determine the polar coordinates of the satellite's position after it completes a full orbit around the Earth.
3) A radar station is tracking an aircraft that is flying at a distance of 500 meters from the origin at an angle of 30 degrees counterclockwise from the positive x –axis. Determine the polar coordinates of the aircraft's position.
4) A target is positioned at a distance of 10 units from the origin at an angle of 60 degrees counterclockwise from the positive x –axis. What are the polar coordinates of the target's position?

Determine the rectangular coordinates of points.

5) $(6, 45°)$
6) $(8, 30°)$
7) $\left(12, \frac{2\pi}{3}\right)$
8) $\left(1, \frac{\pi}{2}\right)$
9) $(5, 60°)$
10) $\left(8, \frac{\pi}{4}\right)$

Sketch the graph of the polar equations on the coordinate plane.

11) $r = 6 - 6\,cos(\theta)$
12) $r = 9 + 5\,cos(\theta)$

Chapter 10: Answers

1) 5 unit
2) $(1000,0°)$
3) $(500,30°)$
4) $(10,60°)$
5) $(4.24,4.24)$
6) $(6.93,4)$
7) $(-6,10.39)$
8) $(0,1)$
9) $(2.5,4.33)$
10) $(5.66, 5.66)$

11)

12)

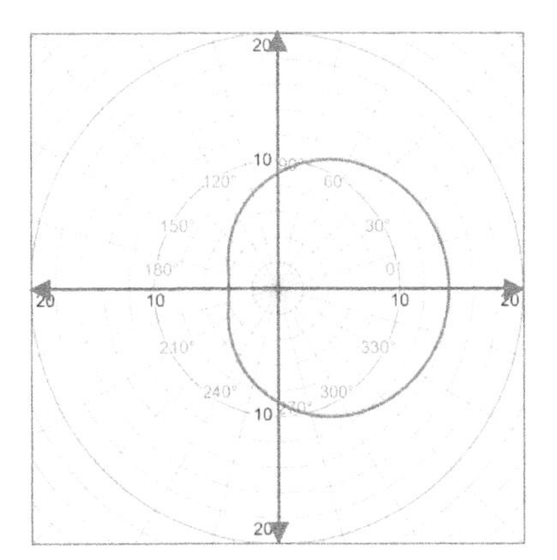

CHAPTER

11 Graphs of Trigonometric Functions

Math topics that you'll learn in this chapter:

- ☑ Graph of the Sine Function
- ☑ Graph of the Cosine Function
- ☑ Amplitude, Period, and Phase Shift
- ☑ Writing the Equation of a Sine Graph
- ☑ Writing the Equation of a Cosine Graph
- ☑ Graph of the Tangent Function
- ☑ Graph of the Cosecant Function
- ☑ Graph of the Secant Function
- ☑ Graph of the Cotangent Function
- ☑ Graph of Inverse of the Sine Function
- ☑ Graph of Inverse of the Cosine Function
- ☑ Graph of Inverse of the Tangent Function
- ☑ Sketching Trigonometric Graphs

Graph of the Sine Function

- The sine function is a set of ordered pairs of real numbers. Each ordered pair can be shown as a point on the coordinate plane.
- To graph the sine function, we plot a portion of the graph using a subset of the real numbers in the interval $0 \le x \le 2\pi$.
- We can see how x and y change by using the graph:
  - By increasing x from 0 to $\frac{\pi}{2}$, y increases from 0 to 1.
  - By increasing x from $\frac{\pi}{2}$ to π, y decreases from 1 to 0.
  - By increasing x from π to $\frac{3\pi}{2}$, y continues to decrease from 0 to -1.
  - By increasing x from $\frac{3\pi}{2}$ to 2π, y increases from -1 to 0.

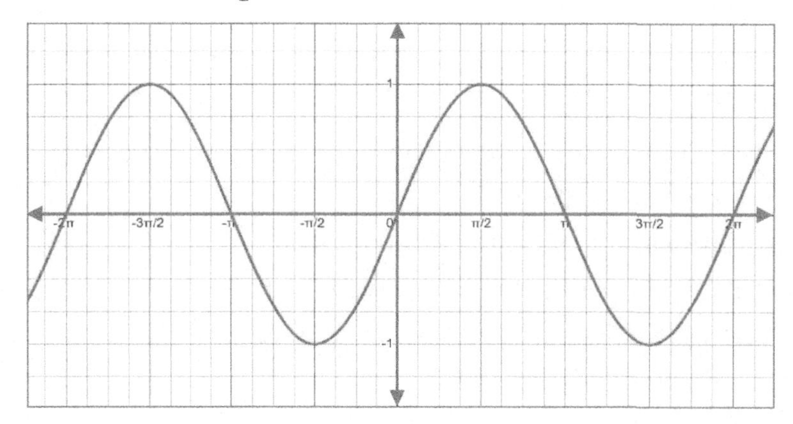

Example:

In the interval $-2\pi \le x \le 0$, for what values of x do $y = \sin x$ increase?

Solution: From the graph, we can see $y = \sin x$ increases in the interval $-2\pi \le x \le -\frac{3\pi}{2}$ and $-\frac{\pi}{2} \le x \le 0$.

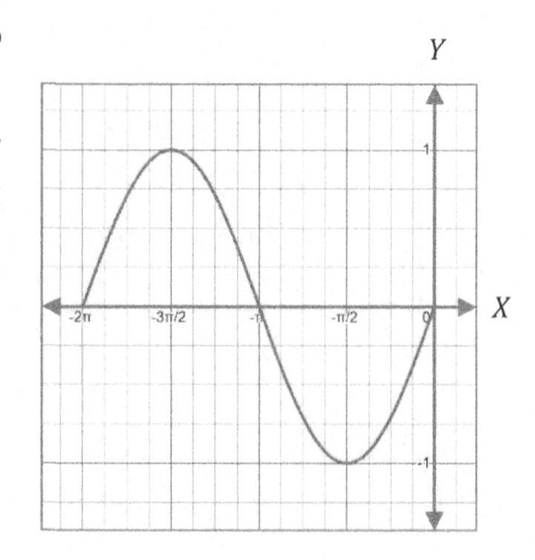

Graph of the Cosine Function

- The cosine function is a set of ordered pairs of real numbers.
- To graph the cosine function, we plot a portion of the graph using a subset of the real numbers in the interval $0 \leq x \leq 2\pi$.
- From the graph, we can know how x and y change:
  - By increasing x from 0 to $\frac{\pi}{2}$, y decreases from 1 to 0.
  - By increasing x from $\frac{\pi}{2}$ to π, y decreases from 0 to -1.
  - By increasing x from π to $\frac{3\pi}{2}$, y increases from -1 to 0.
  - By increasing x from $\frac{3\pi}{2}$ to 2π, y increases from 0 to 1.

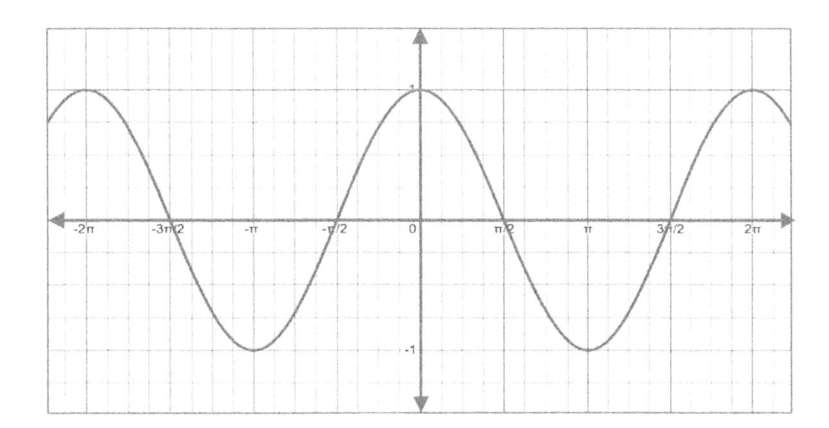

Example:

For what values of x in the interval $0 \leq x \leq 2\pi$, does $y = cos\, x$ have a maximum value?

Solution: From the graph, we can see $y = cos\, x$ at $x = 0$, and $x = 2\pi$ has a maximum value of 1.

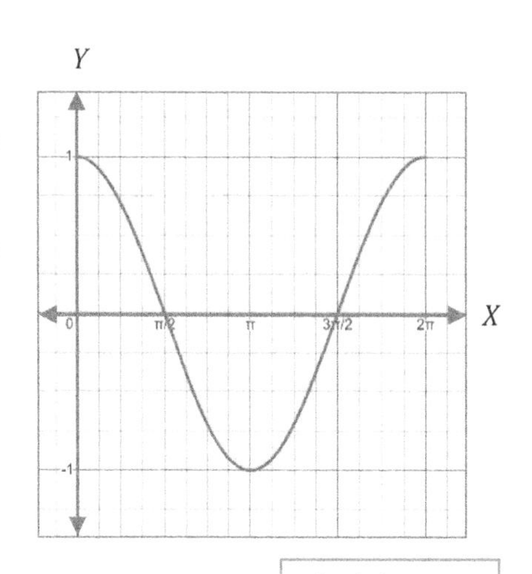

bit.ly/3GW5Gpr

Find more at

Amplitude, Period, and Phase Shift

- For the function $y = a\,sin\,x$, the maximum value of the function is $|a|$, and the minimum value of the function is $-|a|$.
- For the function $y = a\,cos\,x$, the maximum value of the function is $|a|$, and the minimum value of the function is $-|a|$.
- The amplitude of a periodic function is the absolute value of half the difference between the maximum and minimum value of y.
- The difference between the x −coordinates of the endpoints of the interval for one graph cycle is the graph period.
- The period of $y = cos\,bx$ and $y = sin\,bx$ is $\left|\frac{2\pi}{b}\right|$.
- The phase shift is a horizontal translation of a trigonometric function.
- For the $y = a\,sin\,b(x + c)$ and $y = a\,cos\,b(x + c)$, the phase shift is $-c$.

Examples:

Example 1. Determine the amplitude, the period, and the phase shift of $y = -9\,cos(8x + \pi) - 8$.

Solution: Amplitude $= 9$

Period $= \frac{\pi}{4}$

Phase shift $= -\frac{\pi}{8}$

Example 2. Determine the amplitude, the period, and the phase shift of $y = sin(3x - 4) + 5$.

Solution: Amplitude $= 1$

Period $= \frac{2\pi}{3}$

Phase shift $= \frac{4}{3}$

Writing the Equation of a Sine Graph

- Using these steps, we can write an equation for the sine graph:
  - Find a by identifying the maximum and minimum values of y for the function. $a = \frac{maximum - minimum}{2}$
  - Define a basic cycle of the sine graph that starts at $y = 0$, increases to a maximum value, decreases to 0, continues to decrease to the minimum value, and then increases to 0. Find the x −coordinates of the endpoints of this cycle. Write the domain of a cycle in interval notation, $x_0 \le x \le x_1$ or $[x_0, x_1]$.
  - The period of one cycle is $\frac{2\pi}{b} = x_1 - x_0$. Use this formula to find b.
  - The c value is the opposite of the lower endpoint of the interval of the basic cycle: $c = -x_0$.

Example:

Determine the equation of the graph below in the form $y = a\,sin\,bx$.

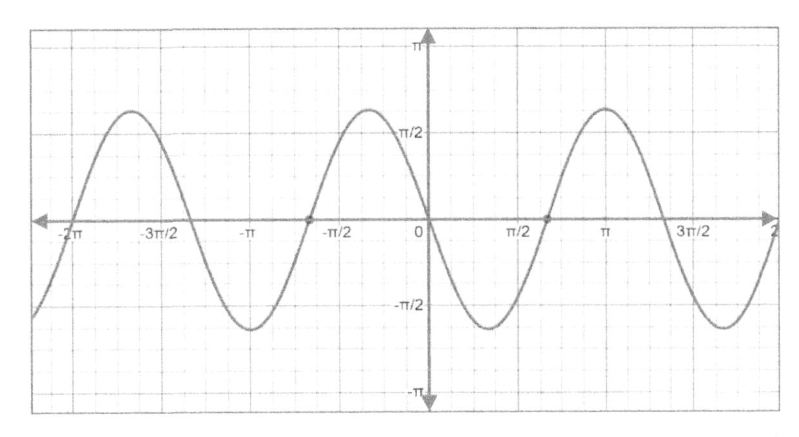

Solution: The max and min values of y are 2 and −2. So, $a = \frac{2-(-2)}{2} = 2$.

The cycle of the curve is in the interval $-\frac{2\pi}{3} \le x \le \frac{2\pi}{3}$. The period is $\frac{2\pi}{3} - \left(-\frac{2\pi}{3}\right)$ or $\frac{4\pi}{3}$. So $\frac{2\pi}{b} = \frac{4\pi}{3} \to b = \frac{3}{2}$.

The c value is $-\left(-\frac{2\pi}{3}\right)$, therefore the phase shift is $-\frac{2\pi}{3}$.

$$y = 2\,sin\frac{3}{2}\left(x + \frac{2\pi}{3}\right)$$

Writing the Equation of a Cosine Graph

- Using these steps, we can write an equation for the cosine graph:
  - Find a by identifying the maximum and minimum values of y for the function. $a = \frac{maximum - minimum}{2}$.
  - Define one basic cycle of the graph that starts at the maximum value, decreases to 0, continues to decrease to the minimum value, increases to 0, and then increases to the maximum value. Find the x −coordinates of the endpoints of this cycle. Write the domain of a cycle in interval notation, $x_0 \leq x \leq x_1$ or $[x_0, x_1]$.
  - The period of one cycle is $\frac{2\pi}{b} = x_1 - x_0$. Use this formula to find b.
  - The c value is the opposite of the lower endpoint of the interval of the basic cycle: $c = -x_0$.

Example:

Determine the equation of the graph below in the form $y = a\cos bx$.

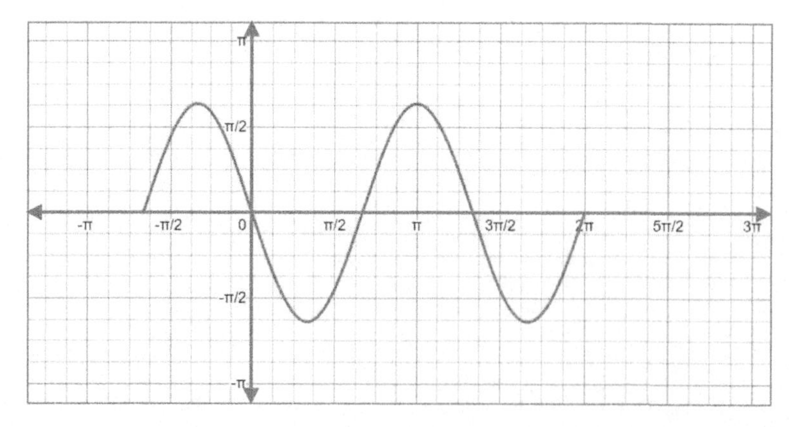

Solution: The max and min values of y are 2 and -2. So, $a = \frac{2-(-2)}{2} = 2$.

The cycle of the curve is in the interval $-\frac{\pi}{3} \leq x \leq \pi$. The period is $\pi - \left(-\frac{\pi}{3}\right)$ or $\frac{4\pi}{3}$.

So, $\frac{2\pi}{b} = \frac{4\pi}{3} \rightarrow b = \frac{3}{2}$.

The c value is $-\left(-\frac{\pi}{3}\right)$, therefore the phase shift is $-\frac{\pi}{3}$.

The equation of the graph is $y = 2\cos\frac{3}{2}\left(x + \frac{\pi}{3}\right)$.

Graph of the Tangent Function

- The tangent graph is a curve that increases through negative values of $tan\, x$ to 0 and then continues to increase through positive values.
- The graph is discontinuous at odd multiples of $\frac{\pi}{2}$ and then repeats the same pattern.
- The tan graph displays a vertical line at $x = \frac{\pi}{2}$ and at every value of x that is an odd multiple of $\frac{\pi}{2}$. These lines are vertical asymptotes.
- The one complete cycle of the curve is in the interval from $x = -\frac{\pi}{2}$ to $x = \frac{\pi}{2}$ and the period of the curve is π.

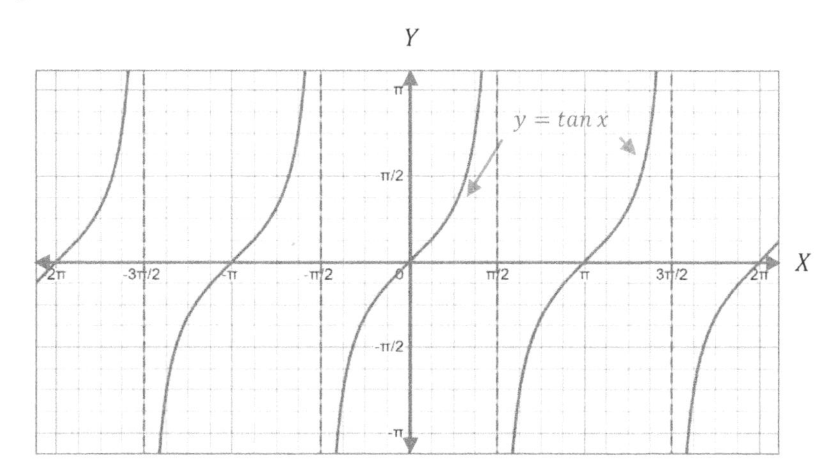

Example:

Draw the graph of $y = tan\left(x - \frac{\pi}{4}\right)$ in the interval of $-\frac{\pi}{4} < x < \frac{3\pi}{4}$.

Solution: The graph of $y = tan\left(x - \frac{\pi}{4}\right)$ is the graph of $y = tan\, x$ but the phase shift is $\frac{\pi}{4}$.

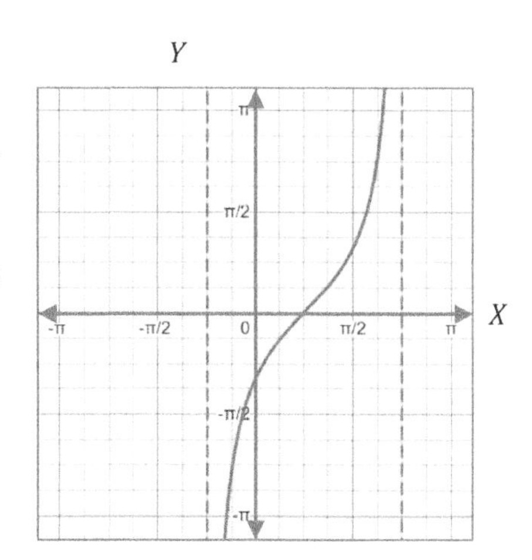

Graph of the Cosecant Function

- The cosecant function is identified in terms of the sine function: $csc\, x = \frac{1}{sin\, x}$.
- To draw the cosecant function graph, use the reciprocals of the sine function values.
- There are reciprocals of the sine function for $-1 \leq sin\, x < 0$, and for $0 < sin\, x < 1$. So, $-\infty < csc\, x \leq -1$, $1 \leq csc\, x < \infty$.
- For values of x that are multiples of π, $sin\, x = 0$, and $csc\, x$ is not defined.
- For integral values of n, the vertical lines on the graph are asymptote at $x = n\pi$.

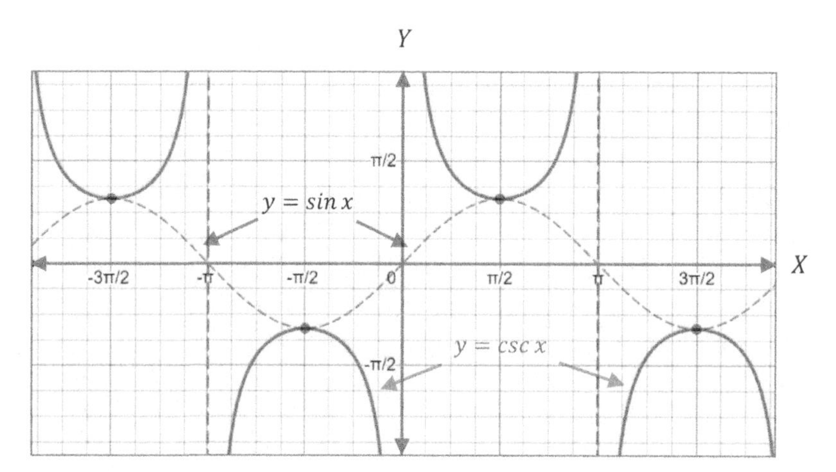

Example:

Draw one period of $y = -3\, csc(4x)$.
Solution: Draw a graph of the function $y = -3\, sin(4x)$. Sketch vertical asymptotes and fill in the cosecant curve in between the asymptotes.

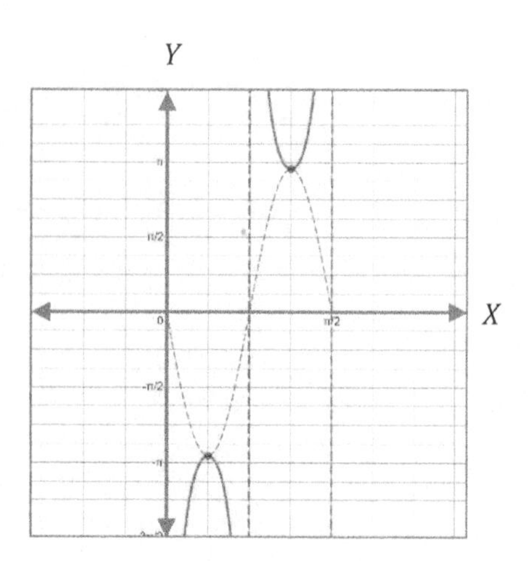

Graph of the Secant Function

- The secant function is identified in terms of the cosine function: $sec\,x = \frac{1}{cos\,x}$.
- To draw the secant function, use reciprocals of the cosine function values.
- There are reciprocals of the cosine function for $-1 \leq cos\,x < 0$, and for $0 < cos\,x \leq 1$. So, $-\infty < sec\,x \leq -1$, $1 \leq sec\,x < \infty$.
- For x values that are odd multiples of $\frac{\pi}{2}$, $cos\,x = 0$, and $sec\,x$ is not defined.
- For integral values of n, the vertical lines on the graph are asymptote at $x = \frac{\pi}{2} + n\pi$.

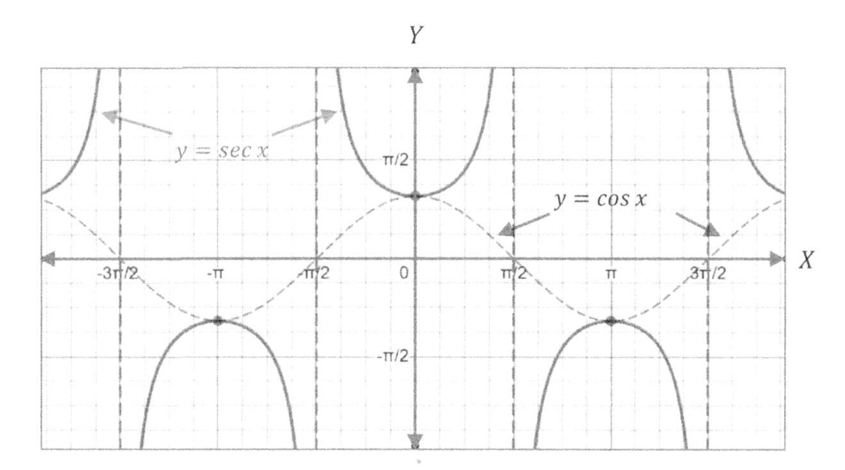

Example:

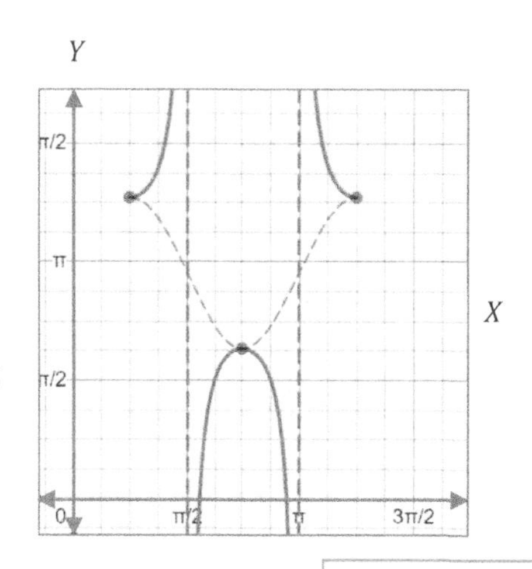

Draw one period of $y = sec\left(2x - \frac{\pi}{2}\right) + 3$.

Solution: Draw a graph of the function.

$$y = cos\left(2x - \frac{\pi}{2}\right) + 3$$

Sketch vertical asymptotes and fill in the secant curve in between the asymptotes.

Graph of the Cotangent Function

- The cotangent function is identified in terms of the tangent function:

$$\cot x = \frac{1}{\tan x}$$

- To draw the cotangent function, use the reciprocals of the tangent function values.
- For values of x that are multiples of π, $\tan x = 0$, and $\cot x$ is not defined.
- For values of x that $\tan x$ is not defined, $\cot x = 0$.
- For integral values of n, the vertical lines on the graph are asymptote at $x = n\pi$.

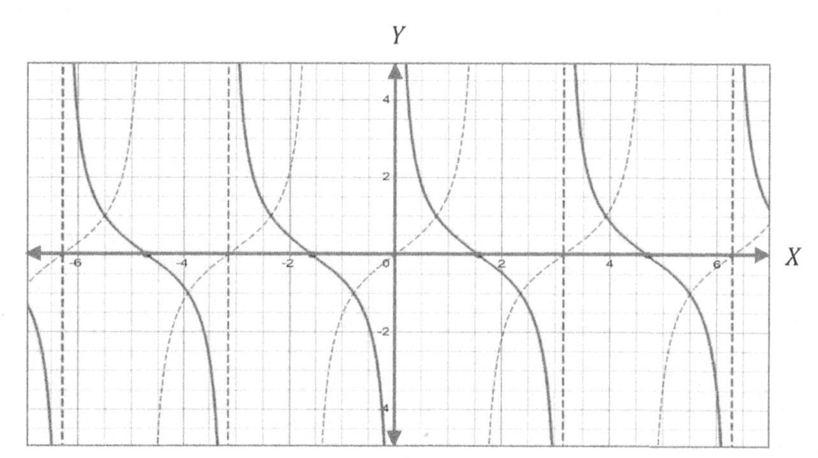

Example:

Draw one period of $y = \cot\left(x + \frac{\pi}{2}\right)$.

Solution: Draw a graph of the function.

$$y = \tan\left(x + \frac{\pi}{2}\right)$$

Sketch vertical asymptotes and fill in the cotangent curve in between the asymptotes.

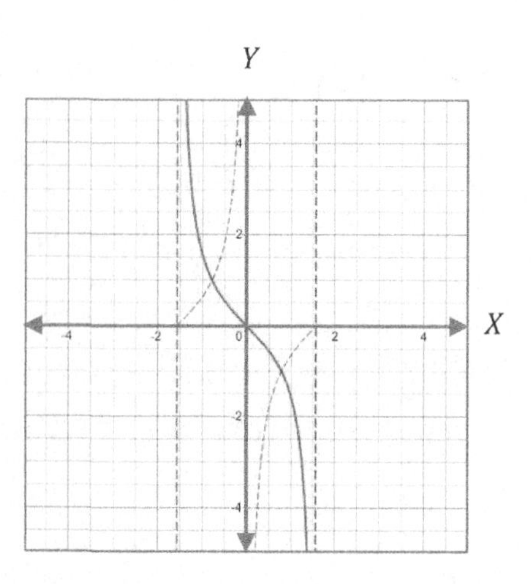

Graph of Inverse of the Sine Function

- If we limit the domain of the sine function to $-\frac{\pi}{2} \leq x \leq \frac{\pi}{2}$, that subset of the sine function is a one-to-one function and has an inverse function.
- When we reflect that subset on the line $y = x$, the image of the function is $y = arcsin\, x$ or $y = sin^{-1}\, x$.

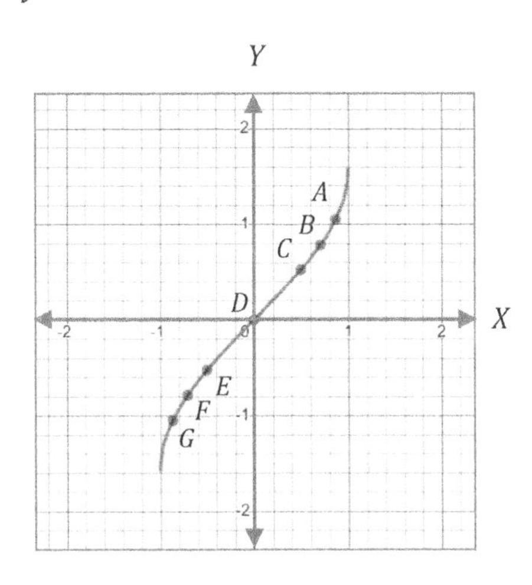

A: $\left(\frac{\sqrt{3}}{2}, \frac{\pi}{3}\right)$

B: $\left(\frac{\sqrt{2}}{2}, \frac{\pi}{4}\right)$

C: $\left(\frac{1}{2}, \frac{\pi}{6}\right)$

D: $(0, 0)$

E: $\left(-\frac{1}{2}, -\frac{\pi}{6}\right)$

F: $\left(-\frac{\sqrt{2}}{2}, -\frac{\pi}{4}\right)$

G: $\left(-\frac{\sqrt{3}}{2}, -\frac{\pi}{3}\right)$

Example:

Draw the function $y = 3\, sin^{-1}(x + 1)$.

Solution: The graph of $y = 3\, sin^{-1}(x + 1)$ is the graph of $y = sin^{-1}\, x$ but the phase shift is -1.

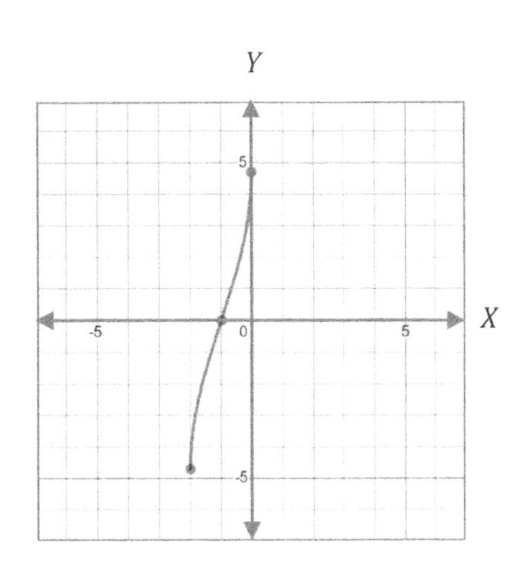

Graph of Inverse of the Cosine Function

- If we limit the domain of the cosine function to $0 \leq x \leq \pi$, that subset of the cosine function is a one-to-one function and has an inverse function.
- When we reflect that subset on the line $y = x$, the image of the function is $y = arccos\, x$ or $y = cos^{-1} x$.

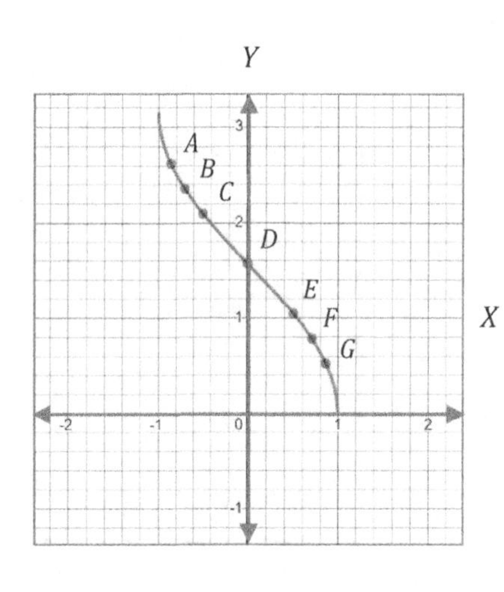

A: $\left(-\frac{\sqrt{3}}{2}, \frac{5\pi}{6}\right)$
B: $\left(-\frac{\sqrt{2}}{2}, \frac{3\pi}{4}\right)$
C: $\left(-\frac{1}{2}, \frac{2\pi}{3}\right)$
D: $\left(0, \frac{\pi}{2}\right)$
E: $\left(\frac{1}{2}, \frac{\pi}{3}\right)$
F: $\left(\frac{\sqrt{2}}{2}, \frac{\pi}{4}\right)$
G: $\left(\frac{\sqrt{3}}{2}, \frac{\pi}{6}\right)$

Example:

Draw the function $y = 2\, cos^{-1}(x - 1)$.

Solution: The graph of $y = 2\, cos^{-1}(x - 1)$ is the graph of $y = cos^{-1} x$ but the phase shift is 1.

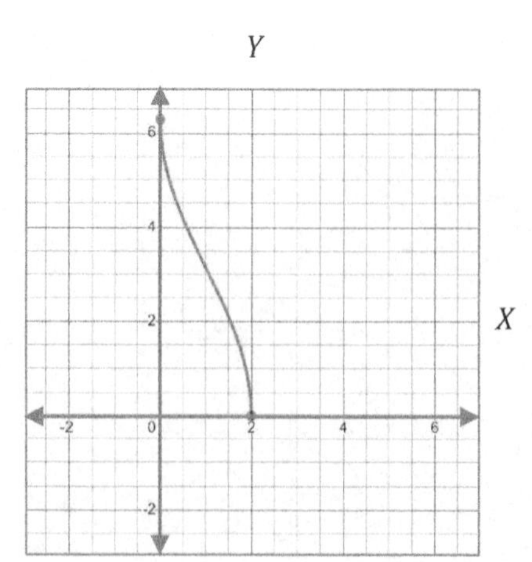

Graph of Inverse of the Tangent Function

- If we limit the domain of the tangent function to $-\frac{\pi}{2} < x < \frac{\pi}{2}$, that subset of the tangent function is a one-to-one function and has an inverse function.
- When we reflect that subset on the line $y = x$, the image of the function is $y = arctan\, x$ or $y = tan^{-1}\, x$.

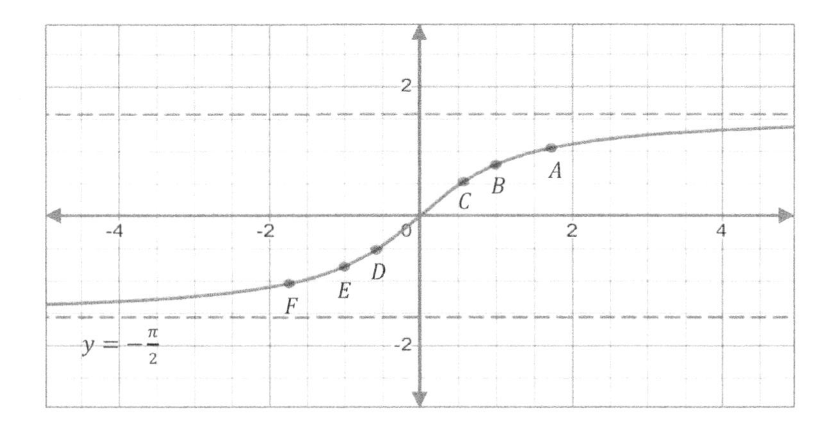

$A: \left(\sqrt{3}, \frac{\pi}{3}\right)$
$B: \left(1, \frac{\pi}{4}\right)$
$C: \left(\frac{\sqrt{3}}{3}, \frac{\pi}{6}\right)$
$D: \left(-\frac{\sqrt{3}}{3}, -\frac{\pi}{6}\right)$
$E: \left(-1, -\frac{\pi}{4}\right)$
$F: \left(-\sqrt{3}, -\frac{\pi}{3}\right)$

Example:

Draw the function $y = -2\, tan^{-1}(x - 1)$.

Solution: The graph of $y = -2\, tan^{-1}(x - 1)$ is the graph of $y = tan^{-1}\, x$ but the phase shift is 1.

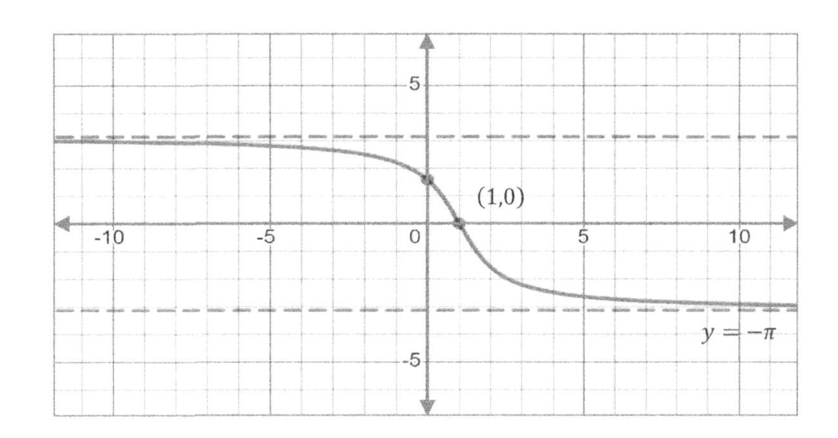

Sketching Trigonometric Graphs

- For $y = a\cos b(x + c)$ and $y = a\sin b(x + c)$:
  - amplitude $= |a|$
  - number of cycles in a 2π interval $= |b|$
  - period of the graph $= \frac{2\pi}{|b|}$
  - phase shift $= -c$
- The values of a, b, and c change the curves of sine and cosine without changing the fundamental shape of a cycle of the graph.

Example:

Draw two cycles of the graph of $y = 2\sin\left(x - \frac{\pi}{4}\right)$.

Solution: For $y = 2\sin\left(x - \frac{\pi}{4}\right)$, $a = 2$, $b = 1$, $c = \frac{\pi}{4}$. So, one cycle starts at $x = \frac{\pi}{4}$. There is a complete cycle in the interval 2π, which is from $\frac{\pi}{4}$ to $\frac{9\pi}{4}$. Divide this interval into four equal intervals and draw one cycle of the sine curve with a maximum of 2 and a minimum of -2.

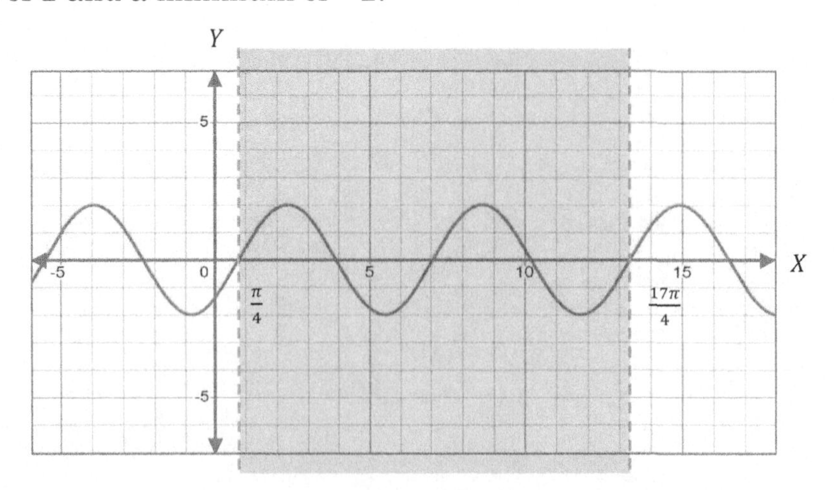

Chapter 11: Practices

✍ Graph the following functions.

1) $y = 2\,sin\,2x$

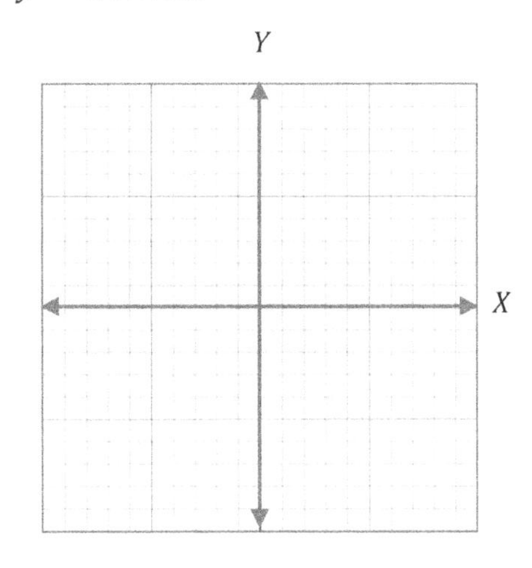

2) $y = -3\,sin\,x$

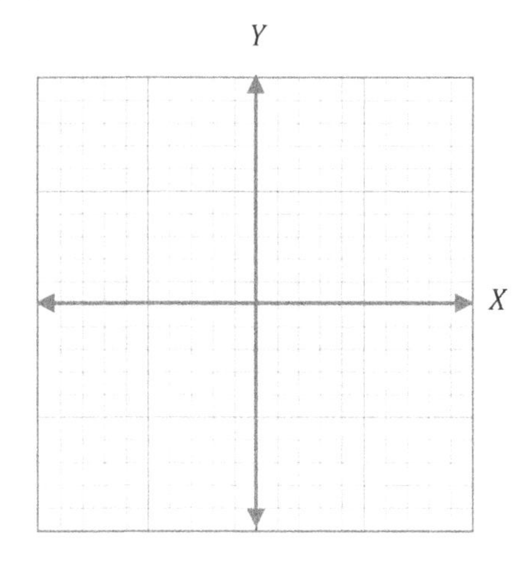

✍ Graph the following functions.

3) $y = -2\,cos\,x$

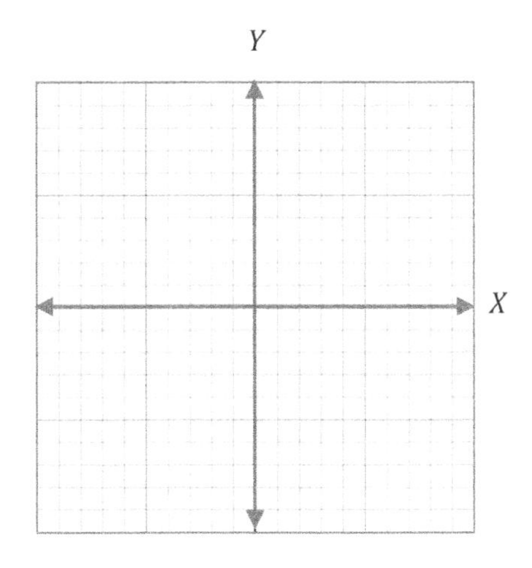

4) $y = 3\,cos\,2x - 2$

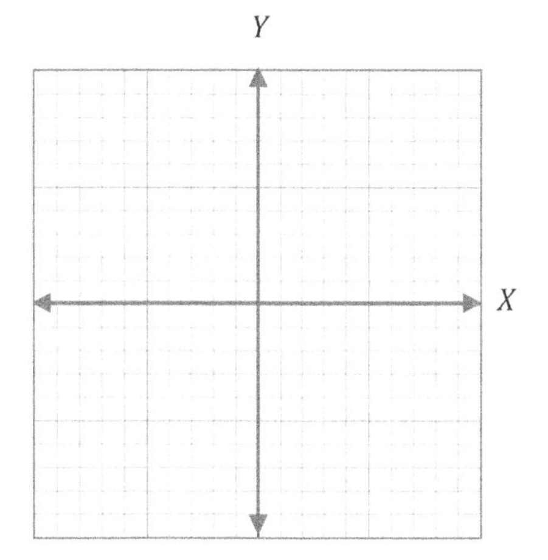

Determine the amplitude, the period, and the phase shift of:

5) $y = sin\left(x - \frac{\pi}{4}\right) - 2$

Amplitude: ____

Period: ____

Phase shift: ____

6) $y = 3\,cos\left(2x - \frac{\pi}{6}\right)$

Amplitude: ____

Period: ____

Phase shift: ____

7) $y = -2\,sin\left(\frac{2}{3}x - \frac{\pi}{3}\right)$

Amplitude: ____

Period: ____

Phase shift: ____

8) $y = \frac{2}{3}cos\left(2x + \frac{\pi}{3}\right) - 2$

Amplitude: ____

Period: ____

Phase shift: ____

Determine the equation of the graph below.

9) ______

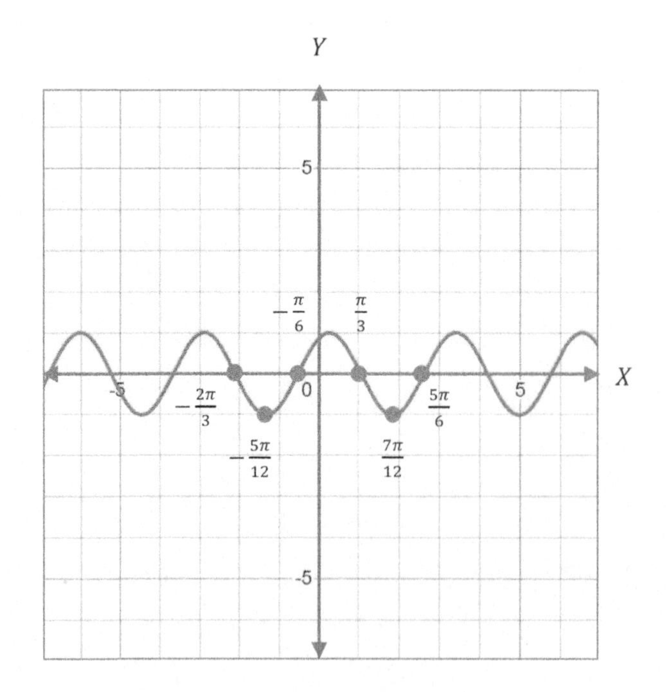

Determine the equation of the graph below.

10) __________

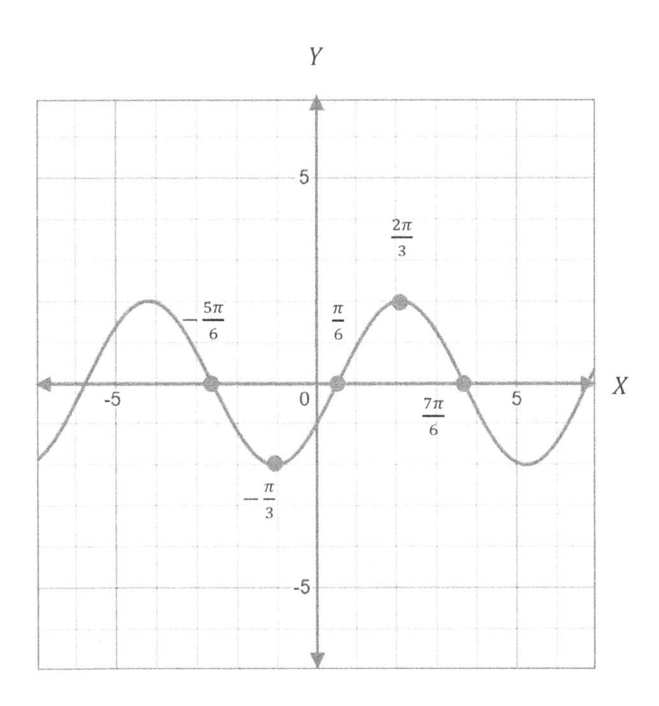

Draw the graph of equations.

11) $y = tan\left(x - \frac{\pi}{4}\right)$

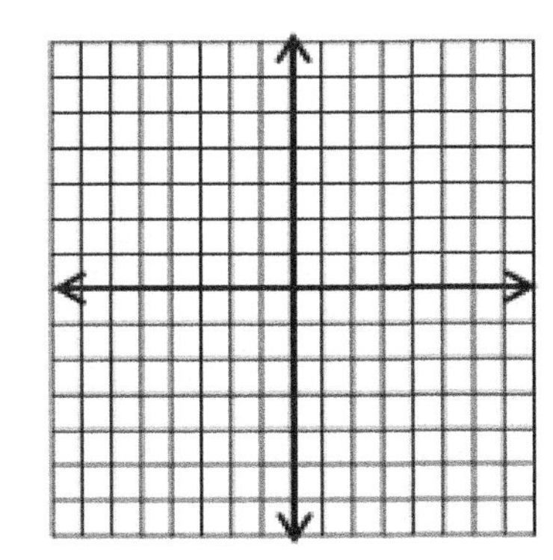

12) $y = 2csc(3x)$

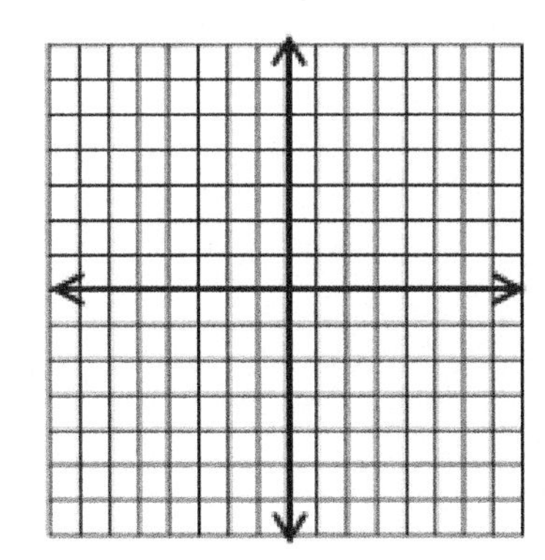

13) $y = 2\,sec\left(-2x + \frac{\pi}{2}\right)$

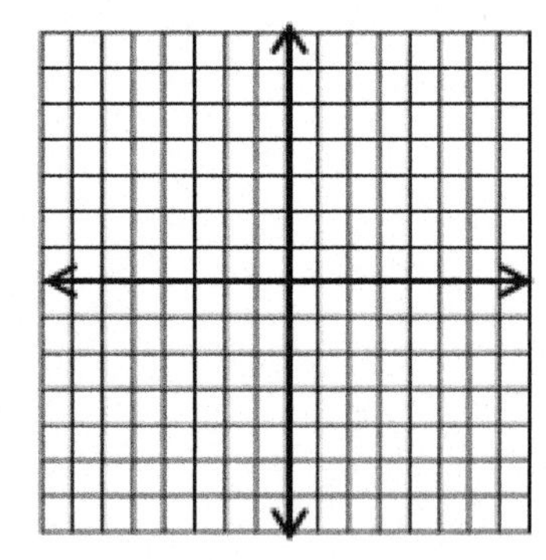

14) $y = cot\left(x - \frac{\pi}{4}\right) + 1$

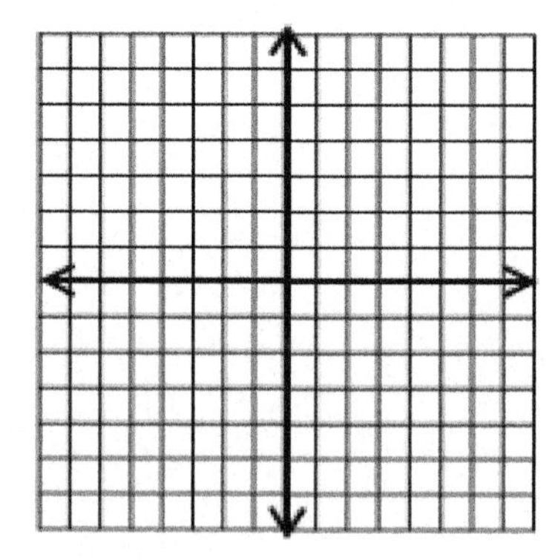

15) $y = 4\,sin^{-1}(x + 4)$

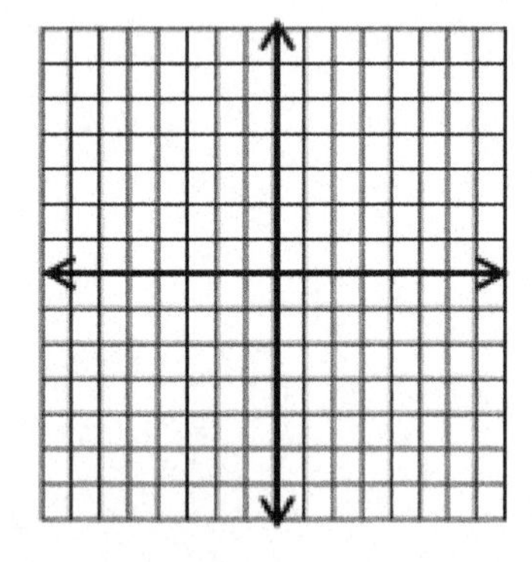

16) $y = 2\,cos^{-1}\left(x - \frac{1}{2}\right)$

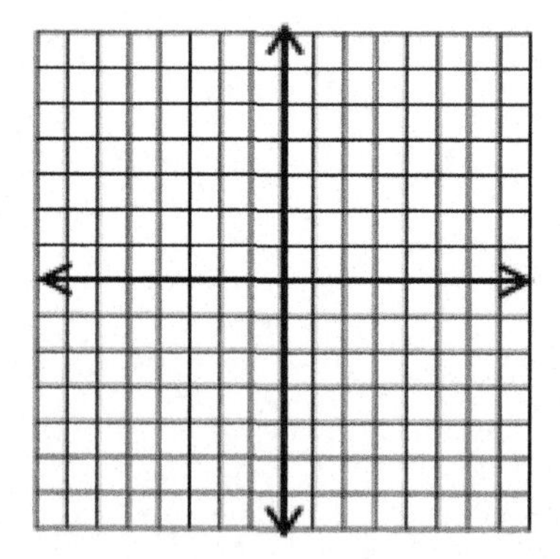

17) $y = 2\,tan^{-1}(x + 2)$

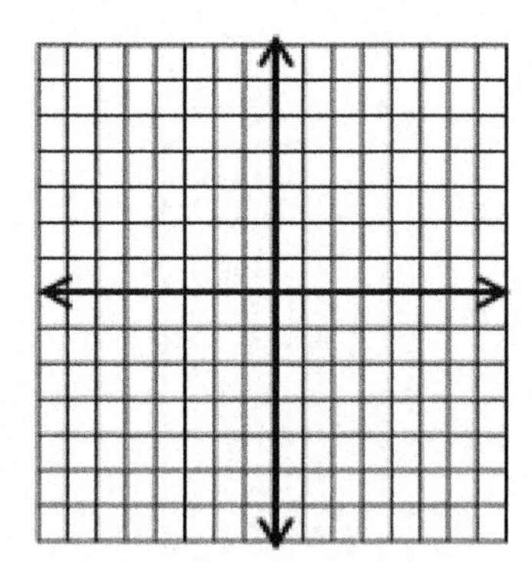

Draw two cycles of the graph.

18) $y = 3\cos\left(x - \frac{\pi}{2}\right)$

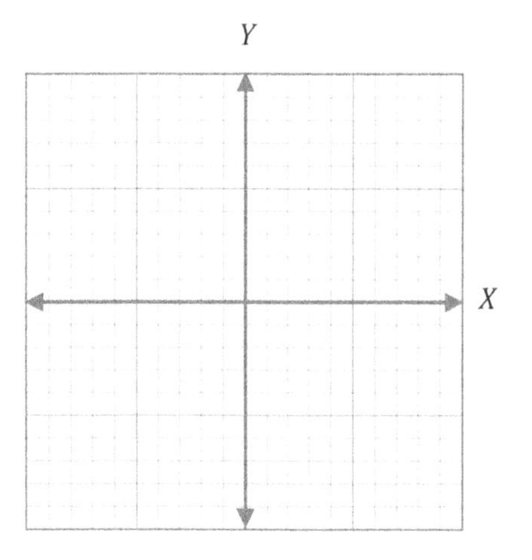

Chapter 11: Answers

1)

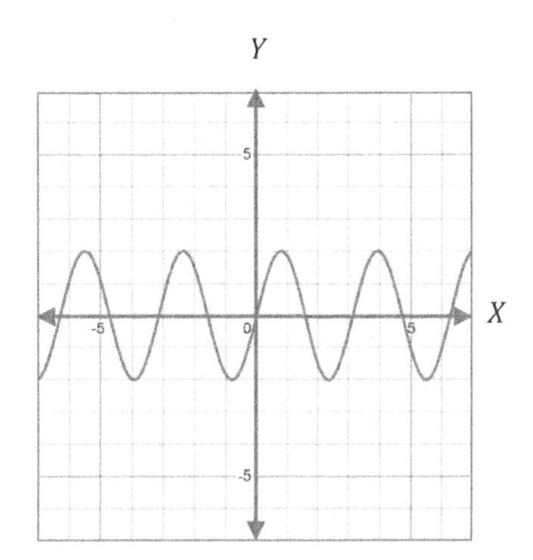

2)

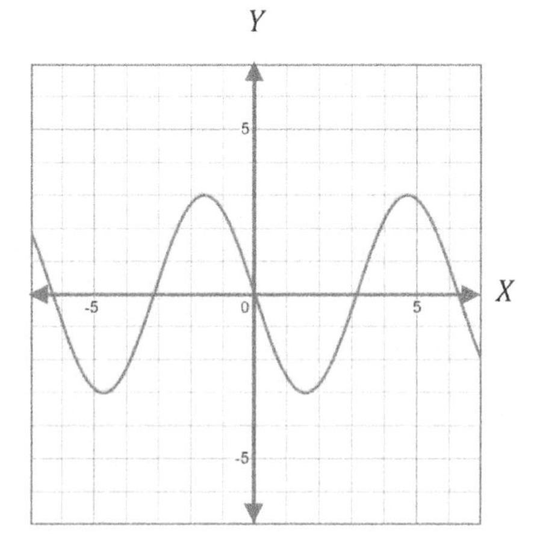

3)

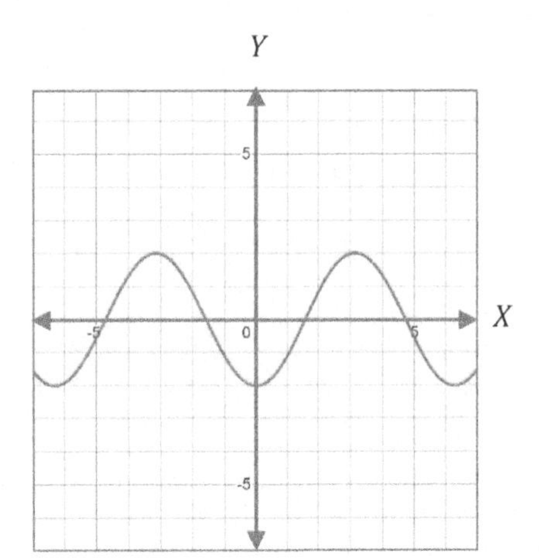

4)

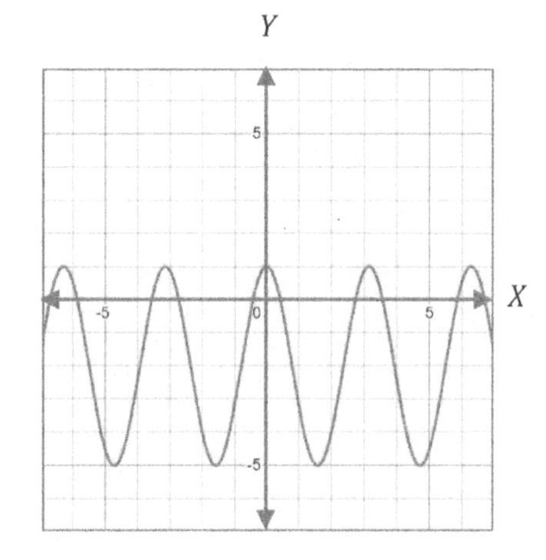

5) Amplitude: 1

Period: 2π

Phase shift: $\frac{\pi}{4}$

6) Amplitude: 3

Period: π

Phase shift: $\frac{\pi}{12}$

7) Amplitude: 2

Period: 3π

Phase shift: $\frac{\pi}{2}$

8) Amplitude: $\frac{2}{3}$

Period: π

Phase shift: $-\frac{\pi}{6}$

9) $y = sin\left(2x + \frac{\pi}{3}\right)$

10) $y = 2\,cos\left(x - \frac{2\pi}{3}\right)$

11)

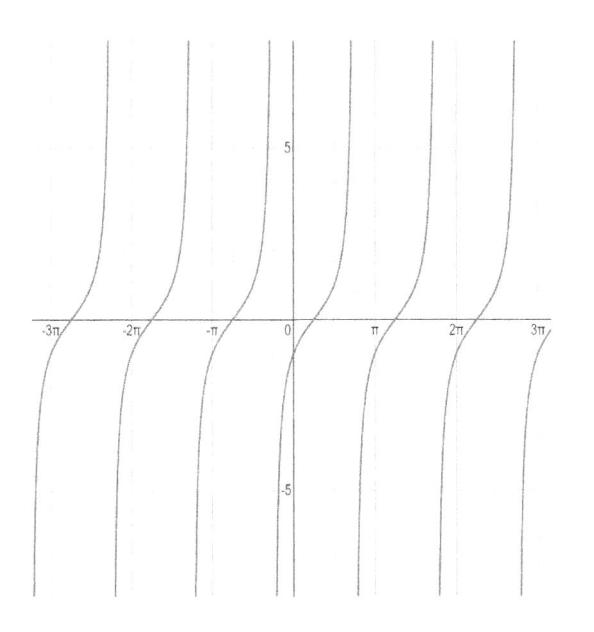

12)

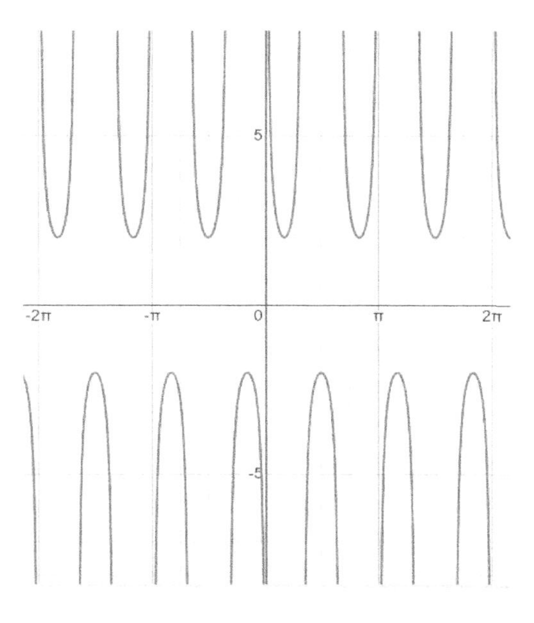

13)

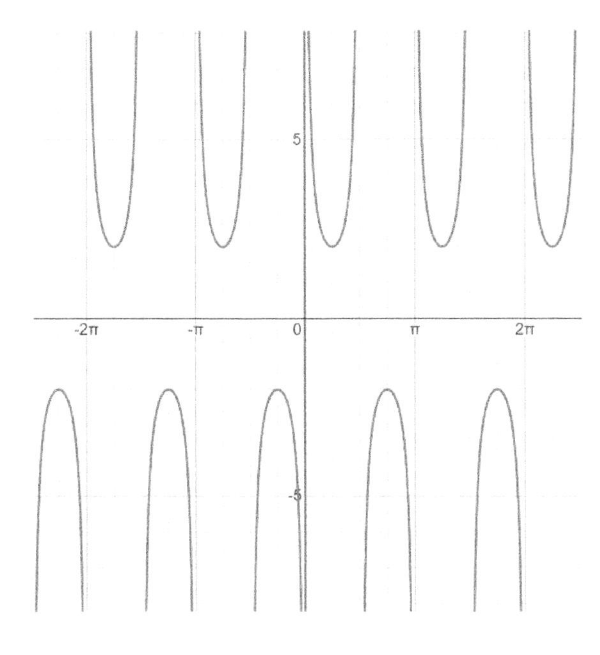

14)

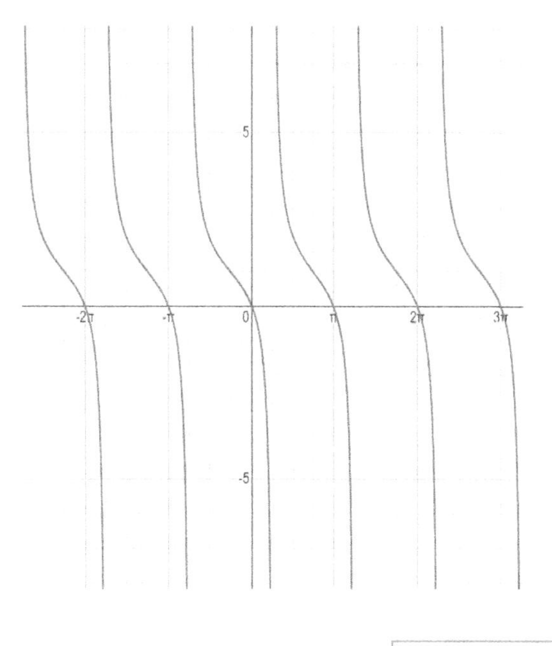

15)

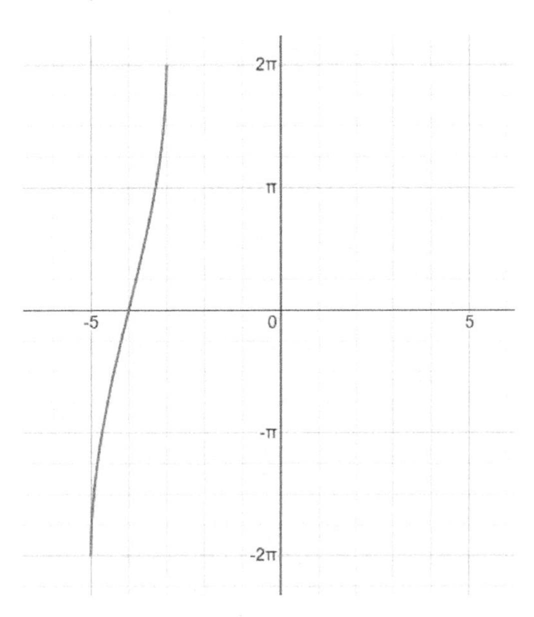

16)

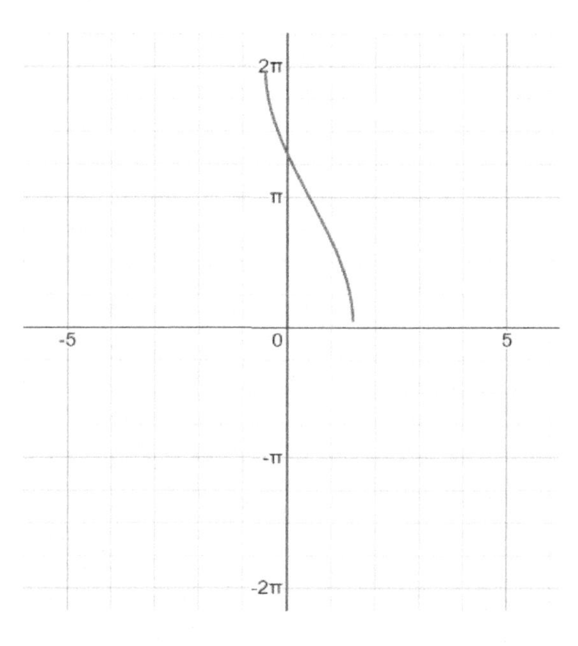

17)

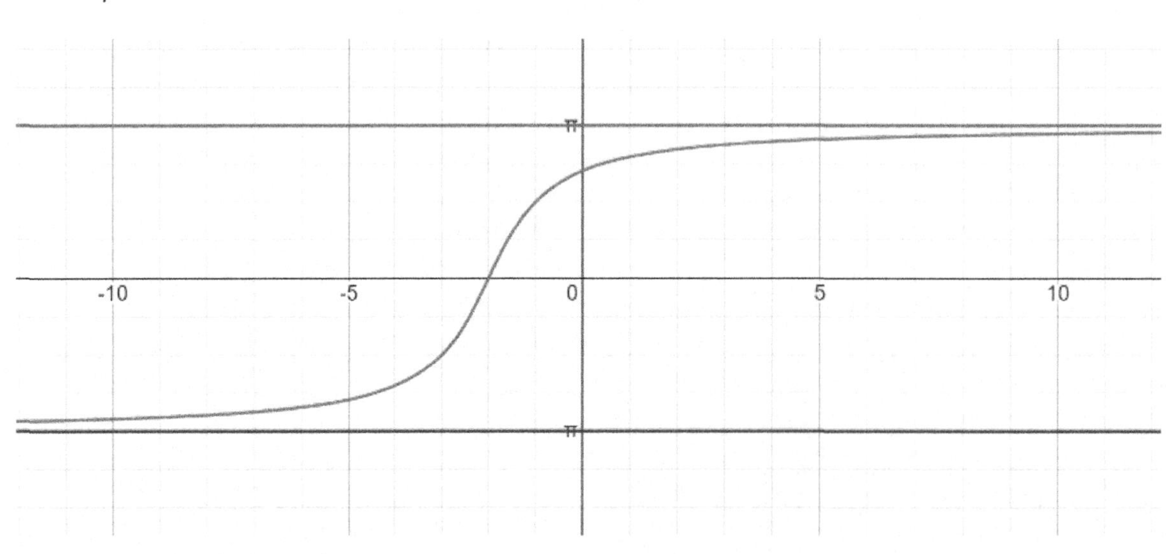

18)

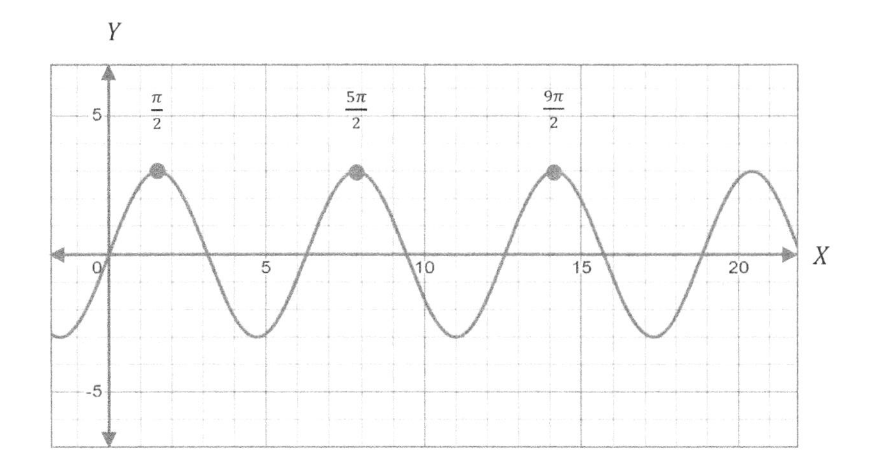

Time to Test

Time to refine your Math skill with a practice test.

In this section, there are two complete Trigonometry Tests. Take these tests to simulate the test day experience. After you've finished, score your test using the answer keys.

Before You Start

- You'll need a pencil a calculator to take the test.
- For each question, there are four possible answers. Choose which one is best.
- It's okay to guess. There is no penalty for wrong answers.
- Use the answer sheet provided to record your answers.
- **Calculator is permitted for Trigonometry Test.**
- After you've finished the test, review the answer key to see where you went wrong.

Good luck!

Trigonometry Practice Test 1

2024

Total number of questions: 50

Time: No time limit

Calculator is permitted for Trigonometry Test.

Trigonometry Practice Test 1 Answer Sheet

Remove (or photocopy) this answer sheet and use it to complete the practice test.

Trigonometry Practice Test 1 Answer Sheet			
1	Ⓐ Ⓑ Ⓒ Ⓓ	26	Ⓐ Ⓑ Ⓒ Ⓓ
2	Ⓐ Ⓑ Ⓒ Ⓓ	27	Ⓐ Ⓑ Ⓒ Ⓓ
3	Ⓐ Ⓑ Ⓒ Ⓓ	28	Ⓐ Ⓑ Ⓒ Ⓓ
4	Ⓐ Ⓑ Ⓒ Ⓓ	29	Ⓐ Ⓑ Ⓒ Ⓓ
5	Ⓐ Ⓑ Ⓒ Ⓓ	30	Ⓐ Ⓑ Ⓒ Ⓓ
6	Ⓐ Ⓑ Ⓒ Ⓓ	31	Ⓐ Ⓑ Ⓒ Ⓓ
7	Ⓐ Ⓑ Ⓒ Ⓓ	32	Ⓐ Ⓑ Ⓒ Ⓓ
8	Ⓐ Ⓑ Ⓒ Ⓓ	33	Ⓐ Ⓑ Ⓒ Ⓓ
9	Ⓐ Ⓑ Ⓒ Ⓓ	34	Ⓐ Ⓑ Ⓒ Ⓓ
10	Ⓐ Ⓑ Ⓒ Ⓓ	35	Ⓐ Ⓑ Ⓒ Ⓓ
11	Ⓐ Ⓑ Ⓒ Ⓓ	36	Ⓐ Ⓑ Ⓒ Ⓓ
12	Ⓐ Ⓑ Ⓒ Ⓓ	37	Ⓐ Ⓑ Ⓒ Ⓓ
13	Ⓐ Ⓑ Ⓒ Ⓓ	38	Ⓐ Ⓑ Ⓒ Ⓓ
14	Ⓐ Ⓑ Ⓒ Ⓓ	39	Ⓐ Ⓑ Ⓒ Ⓓ
15	Ⓐ Ⓑ Ⓒ Ⓓ	40	Ⓐ Ⓑ Ⓒ Ⓓ
16	Ⓐ Ⓑ Ⓒ Ⓓ	41	Ⓐ Ⓑ Ⓒ Ⓓ
17	Ⓐ Ⓑ Ⓒ Ⓓ	42	Ⓐ Ⓑ Ⓒ Ⓓ
18	Ⓐ Ⓑ Ⓒ Ⓓ	43	Ⓐ Ⓑ Ⓒ Ⓓ
19	Ⓐ Ⓑ Ⓒ Ⓓ	44	Ⓐ Ⓑ Ⓒ Ⓓ
20	Ⓐ Ⓑ Ⓒ Ⓓ	45	Ⓐ Ⓑ Ⓒ Ⓓ
21	Ⓐ Ⓑ Ⓒ Ⓓ	46	Ⓐ Ⓑ Ⓒ Ⓓ
22	Ⓐ Ⓑ Ⓒ Ⓓ	47	Ⓐ Ⓑ Ⓒ Ⓓ
23	Ⓐ Ⓑ Ⓒ Ⓓ	48	Ⓐ Ⓑ Ⓒ Ⓓ
24	Ⓐ Ⓑ Ⓒ Ⓓ	49	Ⓐ Ⓑ Ⓒ Ⓓ
25	Ⓐ Ⓑ Ⓒ Ⓓ	50	Ⓐ Ⓑ Ⓒ Ⓓ

1) If $cos^2\theta + 4 = 4\,csc\,\theta$, $0° \leq \theta \leq 90°$, then the value of θ is

A. 30° or 90°

B. 45° or 60°

C. 90°

D. 0°

2) In a right-angled triangle PQR, right-angled at Q, if $PQ = 7$ and $PR - QR = 5$, then $sec\,P + tan\,P$ is

A. $1 + \frac{2}{5}$

B. 1

C. $1 - \frac{2}{5}$

D. $\frac{2}{5}$

3) A regular hexagon can be divided into 6 equilateral triangles. The diagram below shows one of the equilateral triangles. Which one is the high, x, of the equilateral triangle above?

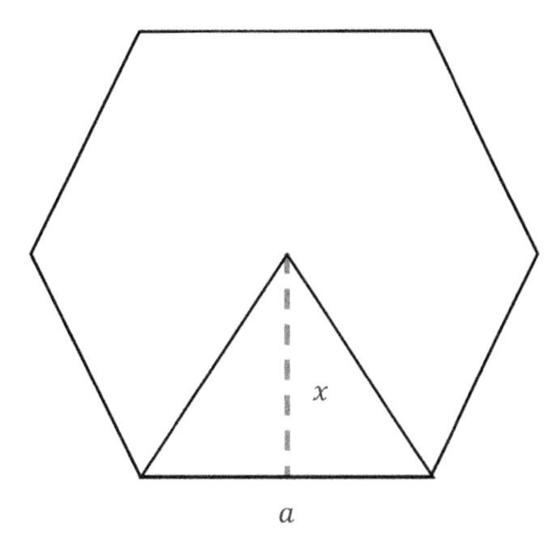

A. $\sqrt{3}a$

B. $\sqrt{2}a$

C. $\frac{\sqrt{3}}{2}a$

D. $\frac{\sqrt{2}}{2}a$

4) If $4\,sin^2\,\theta + 3\,cos^2\,\theta = \frac{7}{2}$ and $0 < \theta < \frac{\pi}{2}$, then $tan\,\theta$ is equal to:

A. -1

B. $\frac{1}{\sqrt{3}}$

C. 1

D. $\sqrt{3}$

5) In ΔABC, $\angle C = 90°$ and $AB = x$, $BC = y$, $CA = z$; then the value of $(sec\,B \cdot tan\,A)$ is

A. $\frac{x}{z}$

B. $\frac{z}{x}$

C. $\frac{y}{x}$

D. $\frac{x}{y}$

6) What is the domain and range of the function $f(x) = \frac{2}{sec(x-\pi)}$?

A. Domain: $\mathbb{R}$, Range: $[-2,2]$

B. Domain: $\mathbb{R} - \left\{\frac{\pi}{2}, \pi\right\}$, Range: $\mathbb{R}$

C. Domain: $\left(-\infty, \frac{\pi}{2}\right) \cup \left(\frac{\pi}{2}, \pi\right) \cup (\pi, +\infty)$, Range: $(-2,2)$

D. Domain: $(-\infty, +\infty)$, Range: $[-1,1]$

7) If $cot(\alpha - \beta) = 1$, $csc(\alpha + \beta) = 2$ and α, β are positive, then the smallest value of α is:

A. 195°

B. 150°

C. 97.5°

D. 45°

8) The minimum value of $4\,sin^2\,\alpha + 5\,cos^2\,\alpha$ is:

A. 4

B. 5

C. 1

D. 0

9) If $tan\,\theta = \frac{5}{12}$ and $sin\,\theta < 0$, then $cos\,\theta = ?$

A. $\frac{12}{13}$

B. $-\frac{5}{13}$

C. $-\frac{12}{13}$

D. $\frac{13}{12}$

10) The value of $cos^2\,240° + cos^2\,300°$ is:

A. $\sqrt{2}$

B. 1

C. $\frac{1}{\sqrt{2}}$

D. $\frac{1}{2}$

11) The value of $cos(60° + \theta) - sin(30° - \theta)$ is:

A. 1

B. 0

C. $2\,cos\,\theta$

D. $2\,sin\,\theta$

12) What is the equation (in standard form) of the following graph?

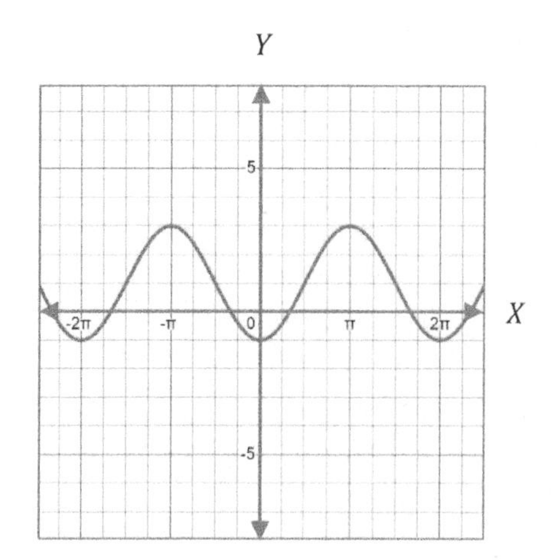

A. $y = 2\,sin\left(x + \frac{\pi}{2}\right)$

B. $y = 2\,sin\left(x - \frac{\pi}{2}\right) + 1$

C. $y = 2\,sin\left(x + \frac{\pi}{2}\right) + 1$

D. $y = 2\,sin\left(x - \frac{\pi}{2}\right) - 1$

13) For which of the following values of x does the equation $cos^2(x) = 1 - x^2$ hold true?

A. $\frac{\pi}{3}$

B. $\frac{\pi}{4}$

C. 1

D. 0

14) If $cos\,\theta = \frac{\sqrt{2}}{2}$ and $0° < \theta < 90°$, then the value of $cot(\theta + 15°)$ is

A. $\sqrt{3}$

B. $\sqrt{2}$

C. $\frac{1}{\sqrt{3}}$

D. $\frac{1}{2}$

15) If $sec\,\theta - tan\,\theta = \sqrt{2}$ $(0° \leq \theta \leq 90°)$, then $tan\,2\theta$ is:

A. Undefined

B. -1

C. 0

D. 1

16) According to the following graph, there is a curve $y = a\,sec(bx) + c$, for the interval $0 \leq x \leq 2\pi$. Based on the graph, what are the values of a, b, and c?

A. $a = 1,\ b = \pi,\ c = 0$

B. $a = 2,\ b = \frac{\pi}{2},\ c = 1$

C. $a = -1,\ b = \pi,\ c = 0$

D. $a = -2,\ b = \frac{\pi}{2},\ c = 1$

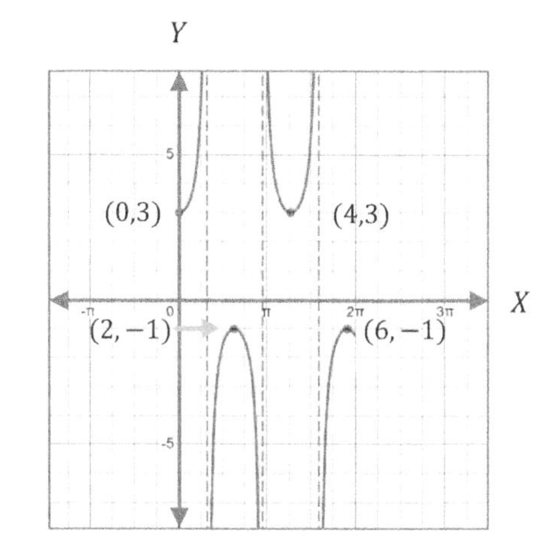

17) A child of height $4\,ft.$ wants to get a kite that is stuck in a $20\,ft.$ high tree. If the child is standing $5\,ft.$ away from the base of the tree, then at what angle should he throw a rock so that it hits the kite?

A. 15°

B. 17°

C. 72°

D. 75°

18) If θ is a positive acute angle and $5\,cos^2(\theta) + sin^2(\theta) = 4$, then the value of θ is:

A. 90°

B. 60°

C. 45°

D. 30°

19) In a triangle ABC, $\angle ABC = 85°$ and $\angle ACB = \frac{\pi}{4}$. The circular measure of $\angle BAC$ is

A. $\frac{7\pi}{9}$ radian

B. $\frac{\pi}{3}$ radian

C. $\frac{5\pi}{18}$ radian

D. $\frac{\pi}{6}$ radian

20) If $cos\,15° = x$, then $(sec\,15° - sin\,75°)$ is equal to

A. $\frac{1-x^2}{x}$

B. $\frac{x}{1-x^2}$

C. $1 - x^2$

D. $\frac{1}{1-x^2}$

21) If φ is an acute angle and $cos(\varphi + 180°) = -\frac{\sqrt{3}}{2}$, then the value of φ in circular measure is:

A. $\frac{\pi}{3}$ radian

B. $\frac{\pi}{6}$ radian

C. $\frac{\pi}{9}$ radian

D. $\frac{2\pi}{3}$ radian

22) If $\alpha + \beta = 120°$ and $\alpha : \beta = 1 : 3$, then the ratio of $sin\,\beta$ to $sin\,\alpha$ is:

A. $1 : 3$

B. $1 : \sqrt{2}$

C. $\sqrt{3} : 1$

D. $2 : 1$

23) If $r \sin\theta = \sqrt{3}$ and $r \cos\theta = 3$, then the values of r and θ are: $(0° \le \theta \le 90°)$

A. $r = 1, \theta = 60°$

B. $r = \sqrt{3}, \theta = 30°$

C. $r = \sqrt{3}, \theta = 60°$

D. $r = 2\sqrt{3}, \theta = 30°$

24) ABC is a triangle. If $\sin\left(\frac{A+B}{2}\right) = \frac{1}{2}$, then the value of $\sin\left(\frac{C}{2}\right)$ is

A. 0

B. $\frac{1}{2}$

C. $\frac{1}{\sqrt{2}}$

D. $\frac{\sqrt{3}}{2}$

25) Find AC in the following triangle. Round your answer to the nearest tenth.

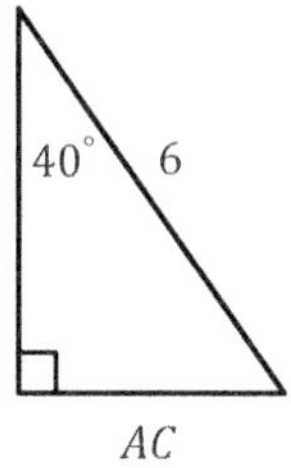

A. 3.86

B. 6

C. 4.59

D. 5.03

26) A woman on the top of a tower, standing on the beach, finds that a boat coming towards her takes 8 minutes for the angle of depression to change from 25° to 50°. How soon will the boat reach the beach?

A. 3 minutes

B. 5 minutes

C. 8 minutes

D. 12 minutes

27) If $\cos x \cdot \cos y + \sin x \cdot \sin y = 1$, then $\sin x - \sin y$ is:

A. -2

B. 0

C. 1

D. 2

28) If $x + sin^2 a + cos^2 a = 3$, then $x =$?

A. 1

B. 2

C. 3

D. 4

29) Which of the following is true for $0° < \theta < 90°$?

A. $sin\,\theta > sin^2\,\theta$

B. $sin\,\theta < sin^2\,\theta$

C. $sin\,\theta \leq sin^2\,\theta$

D. $sin\,\theta \geq sin^2\,\theta$

30) If in a triangle ABC, $tan\,A = cot\,B$, then the value of $sin\,C$ is:

A. 0

B. $\frac{1}{\sqrt{2}}$

C. 1

D. $\frac{\sqrt{3}}{2}$

31) In ΔLMN, $\angle N = 90°$ and $LN: NM = 3:1$. The value of $sin\,L + cot\,M$ is

A. $\frac{3\sqrt{10}+10}{30}$

B. $\frac{3\sqrt{10}+10}{10}$

C. $10 + 3\sqrt{10}$

D. $3 + 10\sqrt{3}$

32) Triangle ABC has a right angle.

Angle ABC is $20°$.

$AB = 16\ cm$

What is the length of BC? (Nearest tenth)

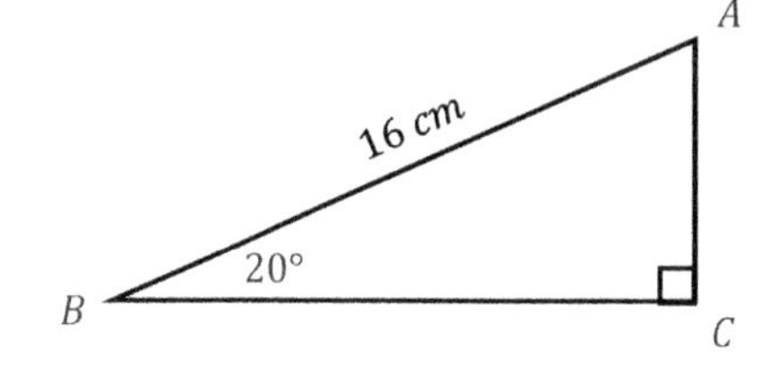

A. 20

B. 15

C. 9.5

D. 5.5

33) If $x\ tan\ 45° + sin\ 60° = csc\ 60°$, then the value of $(x^2 + 1)$ is:

A. $\frac{15}{13}$

B. $\frac{13}{12}$

C. $\frac{12}{13}$

D. $\frac{13}{15}$

34) If $tan\ \theta = \frac{3}{4}$, the value of $\frac{\sqrt{1-sin\ \theta}}{\sqrt{1+sin\ \theta}}$ is:

A. $\frac{2}{3}$

B. $\frac{1}{2}$

C. $\frac{1}{3}$

D. 0

35) The base of a triangle is $14\sqrt{2}\ cm$ and the two angles at the base are $45°$ and $45°$ respectively. The altitude of the triangle is:

A. $7\ cm$

B. $7\sqrt{2}\ cm$

C. $14\ cm$

D. $14\sqrt{2}\ cm$

36) If $2\,cos\left(\frac{\pi x}{3}\right) = x^2 - \frac{1}{x^2}$, then the value of $\left(x + \frac{1}{x}\right)$ is:

A. -1

B. 0

C. 1

D. 2

37) There are two vertical posts, one on each side of a road, just opposite to each other. One post is 150 meters high. From the top of this post, the angle of depression of the top and foot of the other post are 30° and 60° respectively. The height of the other post (in meters) is:

A. 50

B. 100

C. 150

D. 125

38) The value of $126(tan\,45° + 2\,cos^2\,30° + 3\,tan\,45° + 4\,cos^2\,30° + \cdots + 23\,tan\,45° + 24\,cos^2\,30°)$ is:

A. an integer but not a perfect square

B. a rational number but not an integer

C. a perfect square of an integer

D. irrational

39) What is the value of $cos\,30^{\circ}$?

A. $\frac{\sqrt{2}}{2}$

B. $\frac{1}{2}$

C. $-\frac{1}{2}$

D. $\frac{\sqrt{3}}{2}$

40) If the sum and difference of two angles are $120°$ and $\frac{\pi}{6}$ respectively, then the value of the angles in degree measure are:

A. $90°, 30°$

B. $60°, 45°$

C. $45°, 75°$

D. $30°, 15°$

41) Find the value of x in the following triangle. (Round your answer to the closest whole number.)

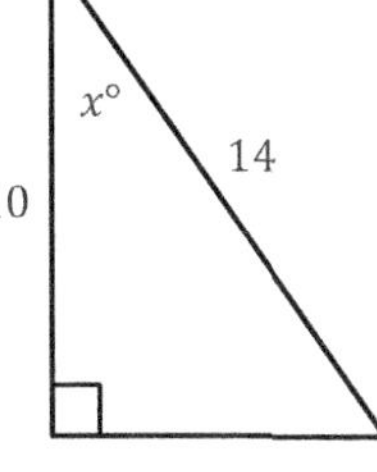

A. 140

B. 45

C. 44

D. 24

42) What is the value of x in the following diagram? (There are 2 supplementary angles in the diagram.)

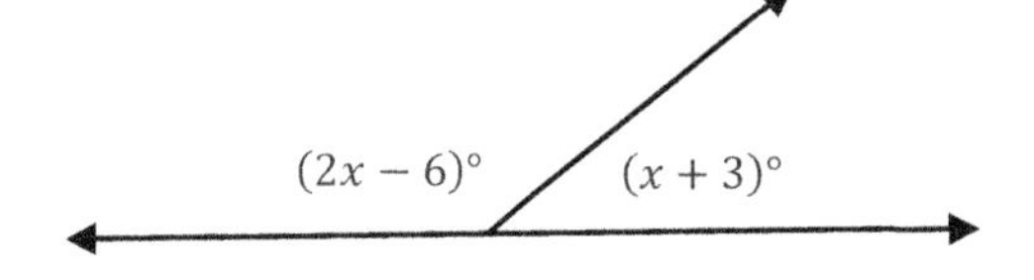

A. 54

B. 61

C. 45

D. 90

43) Find side AC in the following triangle. Round your answer to the nearest tenth.

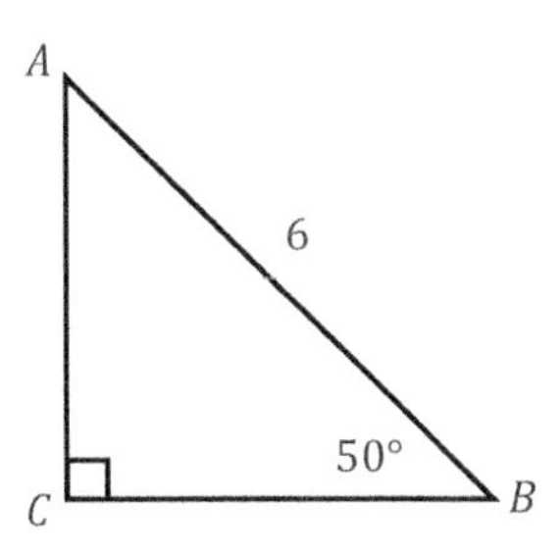

A. 7.14

B. 4.6

C. 3.8

D. 6

44) If $x\,tan\,30° = y\,sec\,60°$, then $\frac{x^4}{y^4}$ is equal to:

A. 2^2

B. 4^2

C. 6^2

D. 12^2

45) Find $tan\frac{2\pi}{3}$?

A. $\sqrt{3}$

B. $-\frac{\sqrt{3}}{3}$

C. $-\sqrt{3}$

D. $\frac{\sqrt{3}}{3}$

46) $2\,sin^2\,\theta + sin\,\theta - 1 = 0$ will be true if

A. $0 \leq \theta < 90°$

B. $0° < \theta < 90°$

C. $\theta = 30°$

D. $\theta = 15°$

47) In triangle ABC, $\angle B = \frac{\pi}{6}$, $\angle C = \frac{\pi}{3}$, and D divides BC internally in the ratio $1:2$. The value of $\frac{sin\,\angle BAD}{sin\,\angle CAD}$ is equal to

A. $\frac{1}{2\sqrt{2}}$

B. $\frac{1}{2\sqrt{3}}$

C. $\frac{1}{3\sqrt{2}}$

D. $\frac{1}{3\sqrt{3}}$

48) What is the value of $\sin\left(\frac{11\pi}{4}\right)$?

A. $-\frac{2}{\sqrt{3}}$

B. $-\frac{1}{\sqrt{2}}$

C. $\frac{1}{\sqrt{2}}$

D. $\frac{2}{\sqrt{3}}$

49) Two right-angled triangles are shown below.

NO is 12 cm

MN is 6 cm

Angle NMP is 60°

Find the size of angle MNO.

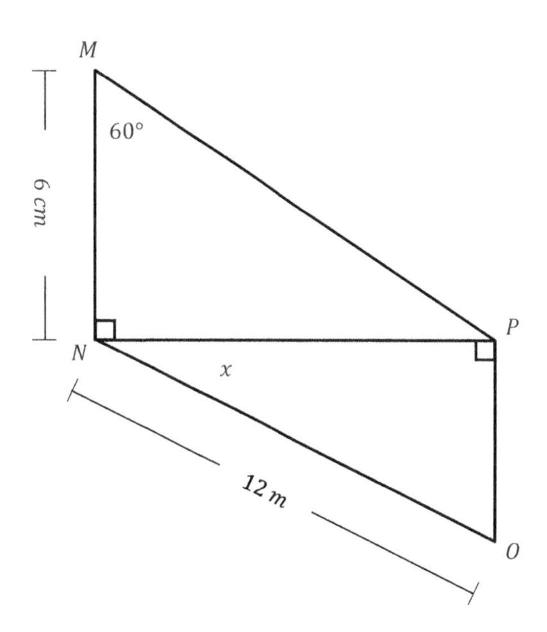

A. 30°

B. 60°

C. 90°

D. 120°

50) If $3x - 2\,sin^2\,a - 2\,cos^2\,a = 4$, then $x =$?

A. 1

B. 2

C. 3

D. 4

End of Trigonometry Practice Test 1

Trigonometry Practice Test 2

2024

Total number of questions: 50

Time: No time limit

Calculator is permitted for Trigonometry Test.

Trigonometry Practice Test 2 Answer Sheet

Remove (or photocopy) this answer sheet and use it to complete the practice test.

Trigonometry Practice Test 2 Answer Sheet			
1	Ⓐ Ⓑ Ⓒ Ⓓ	26	Ⓐ Ⓑ Ⓒ Ⓓ
2	Ⓐ Ⓑ Ⓒ Ⓓ	27	Ⓐ Ⓑ Ⓒ Ⓓ
3	Ⓐ Ⓑ Ⓒ Ⓓ	28	Ⓐ Ⓑ Ⓒ Ⓓ
4	Ⓐ Ⓑ Ⓒ Ⓓ	29	Ⓐ Ⓑ Ⓒ Ⓓ
5	Ⓐ Ⓑ Ⓒ Ⓓ	30	Ⓐ Ⓑ Ⓒ Ⓓ
6	Ⓐ Ⓑ Ⓒ Ⓓ	31	Ⓐ Ⓑ Ⓒ Ⓓ
7	Ⓐ Ⓑ Ⓒ Ⓓ	32	Ⓐ Ⓑ Ⓒ Ⓓ
8	Ⓐ Ⓑ Ⓒ Ⓓ	33	Ⓐ Ⓑ Ⓒ Ⓓ
9	Ⓐ Ⓑ Ⓒ Ⓓ	34	Ⓐ Ⓑ Ⓒ Ⓓ
10	Ⓐ Ⓑ Ⓒ Ⓓ	35	Ⓐ Ⓑ Ⓒ Ⓓ
11	Ⓐ Ⓑ Ⓒ Ⓓ	36	Ⓐ Ⓑ Ⓒ Ⓓ
12	Ⓐ Ⓑ Ⓒ Ⓓ	37	Ⓐ Ⓑ Ⓒ Ⓓ
13	Ⓐ Ⓑ Ⓒ Ⓓ	38	Ⓐ Ⓑ Ⓒ Ⓓ
14	Ⓐ Ⓑ Ⓒ Ⓓ	39	Ⓐ Ⓑ Ⓒ Ⓓ
15	Ⓐ Ⓑ Ⓒ Ⓓ	40	Ⓐ Ⓑ Ⓒ Ⓓ
16	Ⓐ Ⓑ Ⓒ Ⓓ	41	Ⓐ Ⓑ Ⓒ Ⓓ
17	Ⓐ Ⓑ Ⓒ Ⓓ	42	Ⓐ Ⓑ Ⓒ Ⓓ
18	Ⓐ Ⓑ Ⓒ Ⓓ	43	Ⓐ Ⓑ Ⓒ Ⓓ
19	Ⓐ Ⓑ Ⓒ Ⓓ	44	Ⓐ Ⓑ Ⓒ Ⓓ
20	Ⓐ Ⓑ Ⓒ Ⓓ	45	Ⓐ Ⓑ Ⓒ Ⓓ
21	Ⓐ Ⓑ Ⓒ Ⓓ	46	Ⓐ Ⓑ Ⓒ Ⓓ
22	Ⓐ Ⓑ Ⓒ Ⓓ	47	Ⓐ Ⓑ Ⓒ Ⓓ
23	Ⓐ Ⓑ Ⓒ Ⓓ	48	Ⓐ Ⓑ Ⓒ Ⓓ
24	Ⓐ Ⓑ Ⓒ Ⓓ	49	Ⓐ Ⓑ Ⓒ Ⓓ
25	Ⓐ Ⓑ Ⓒ Ⓓ	50	Ⓐ Ⓑ Ⓒ Ⓓ

1) What is the domain and range of the function $f(x) = 2 - 3\sin\left(2x - \frac{\pi}{3}\right)$?

A. Domain: $\left[\frac{\pi}{3}, +\infty\right)$, Range: $[-1,5]$

B. Domain: $(-\infty, +\infty)$, Range: $[-5,1]$

C. Domain: $\mathbb{R} - \frac{\pi}{3}$, Range: $[-5,1]$

D. Domain: $\mathbb{R}$, Range: $[-1,5]$

2) Which statement best describes the equation $y = \frac{1}{cos\left(x - \frac{\pi}{2}\right)} + 4$?

A. The function has vertical asymptote at $x = n\frac{\pi}{2}$; n is an integer.

B. The function has horizontal asymptote at $y = 5$ and $y = 3$.

C. It represents a secant function, $y = sec\,x$, translated $\frac{\pi}{2}$ units to the left.

D. It represents a cosine function, $y = csc\,x$, translated 4 units upwards.

3) If $tan\,x = \frac{8}{15}$, then $sin\,x = ?$

A. $\frac{15}{8}$

B. $\frac{15}{17}$

C. $\frac{8}{17}$

D. $-\frac{15}{17}$

4) Evaluate: $4\,cos\,70°\,csc\,20° + 3\,cos\,60°\,csc\,30°$.

A. 7

B. 5

C. 4

D. 1

5) Which function represents this graph?

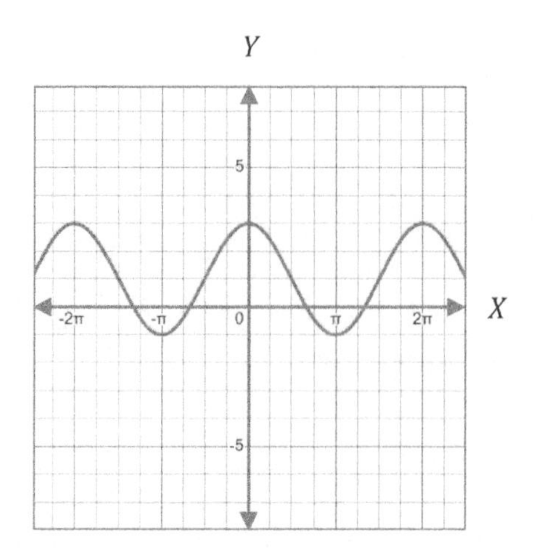

A. $y = 2\,sec(x)$

B. $y = cos(x) + 1$

C. $y = tan(2x) - 1$

D. $y = 2\,cos(x) - 1$

6) What are the zeroes of the function $f(x) = sin^3(x) + 6\,sin^2(x) + 8\,sin(x)$, $0 \le x \le \pi$?

A. $\{0, \pi\}$

B. $\left\{0, \frac{\pi}{6}, \frac{\pi}{3}\right\}$

C. $\left\{0, \frac{\pi}{2}, \frac{\pi}{4}, \pi\right\}$

D. No roots

7) What is the inverse of $f(x) = 1 - sin(x)$?

A. $f^{-1}(x) = sin(1 - x)$

B. $f^{-1}(x) = arcsin(1 - x)$

C. $f^{-1}(x) = 1 - arcsin(x)$

D. $f^{-1}(x) = arcsin(x - 1)$

8) In circular measure, the value of $15°$ is

A. $\frac{\pi}{12}$

B. $\frac{\pi}{8}$

C. $\frac{\pi}{4}$

D. $\frac{\pi}{6}$

9) A ladder leans against a wall forming a 60° angle between the ground and the ladder. If the bottom of the ladder is 30 feet away from the wall, how long is the ladder?

A. $30ft$

B. $60ft$

C. $30\sqrt{3}ft$

D. $30\sqrt{2}ft$

10) Which graph corresponds to $f(x) = tan\left(x - \frac{\pi}{2}\right) + 2$, when $0 \le x \le \pi$?

A.

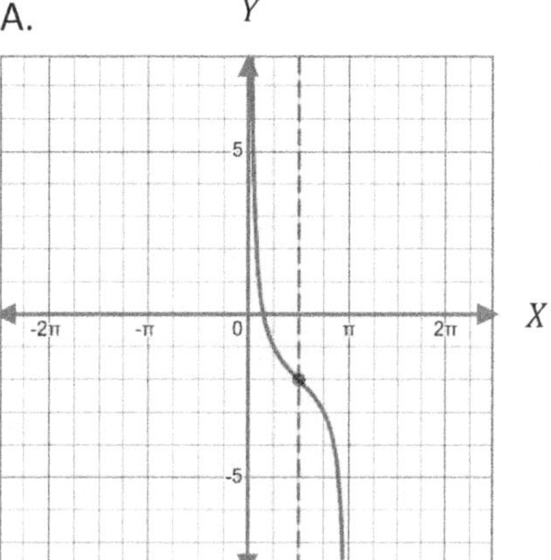

B.

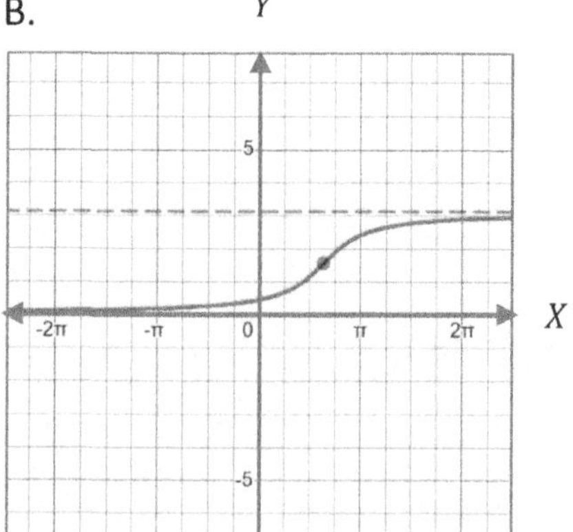

C.

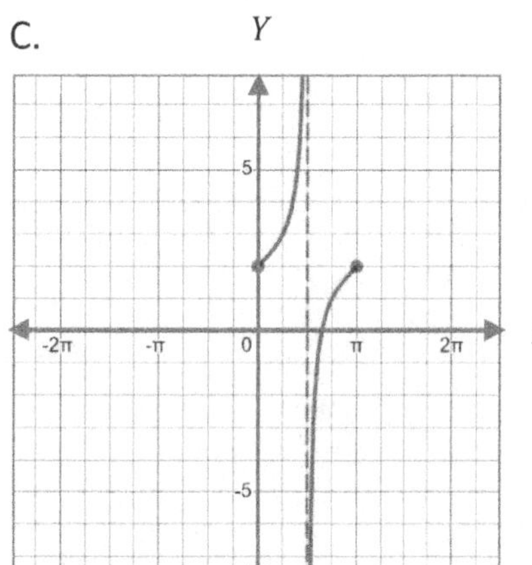

D.

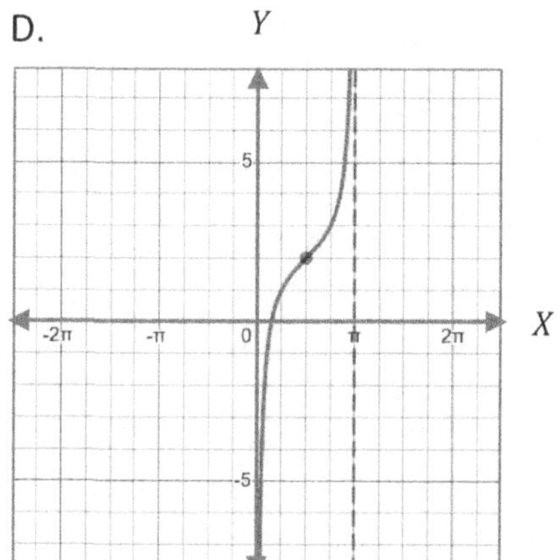

11) The diagram shows two right-angled triangles.

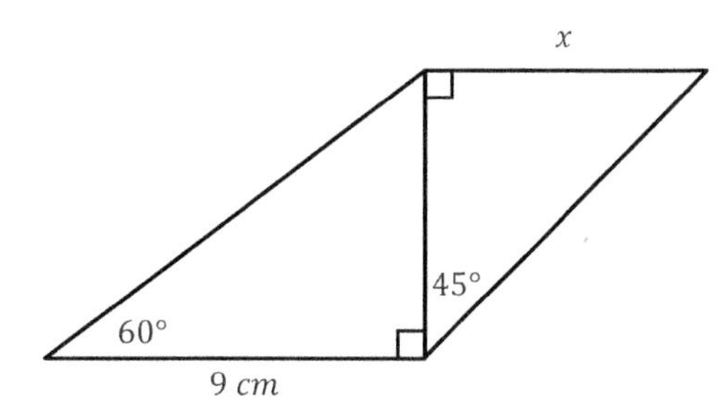

Find the value of x.

A. $\frac{9}{\sqrt{2}}$

B. 9

C. $9\sqrt{2}$

D. $9\sqrt{3}$

12) The two sides of a river are straight and parallel. X, Y, Z are three individuals of whom X stands on one side and Y and Z on the opposite side. Y finds the angle $\angle XYZ$ to be 45°, while Z finds the angle $\angle XZY$ to be 30°. If Y and Z are 120 meters apart, the width of the river is

A. $\frac{120}{\sqrt{3}}$ meters

B. $\frac{120}{\sqrt{3}+1}$ meters

C. $\frac{\sqrt{3}+1}{120}$ meters

D. $\frac{\sqrt{3}}{120}$ meters

13) What is the inverse of $f(x) = cos^2\left(\frac{1}{2}x - 1\right)$?

A. $f^{-1}(x) = 2\,arccos(x)$

B. $f^{-1}(x) = 2\sqrt{arccos(x)} + 2$

C. $f^{-1}(x) = 2\,arccos(\sqrt{x}) + 2$

D. $f^{-1}(x) = 2\,tan(\sqrt{x}) - 2$

14) Which statement best describes these two functions?

$$f(x) = \cos x + 4$$
$$g(x) = 2 - \sin^2 x$$

A. They have no common points.

B. They have the same x −intercepts.

C. The maximum of $f(x)$ is the same as the maximum of $g(x)$.

D. They have the same minimum.

15) If $\sin\theta \times \cos\theta = 0.3$, the value of $\cos^2\theta - \sin^2\theta$ is where $0° < \theta < 90°$

A. 1.2

B. 1

C. 0.9

D. 0.8

16) If $\cos\left(\frac{\pi x}{2}\right) = x^2 - x + 1$, then the value of x is

A. −1

B. 0

C. 1

D. None of these

17) Which graph represents the inverse of $y = sin\left(x - \frac{\pi}{3}\right)$ over the interval $\left[-\frac{\pi}{6}, \frac{5\pi}{6}\right]$?

A. Y

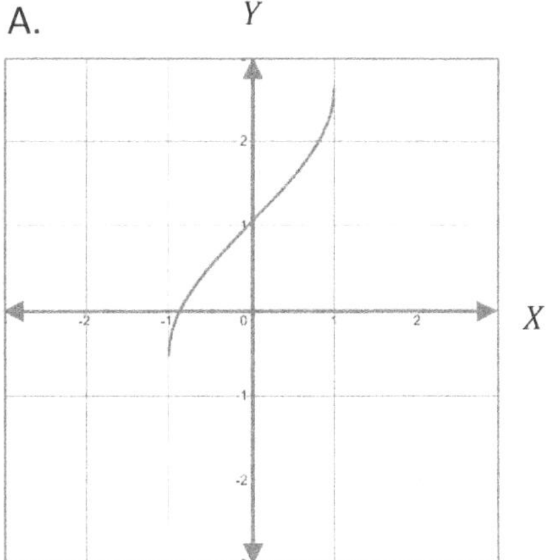

X

B. Y

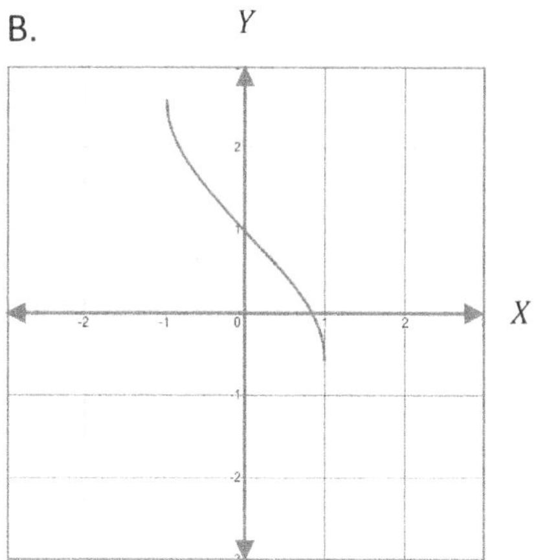

X

C. Y

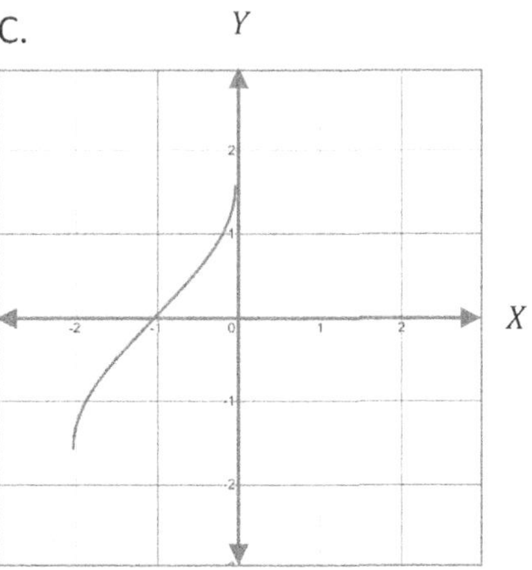

X

D. Y

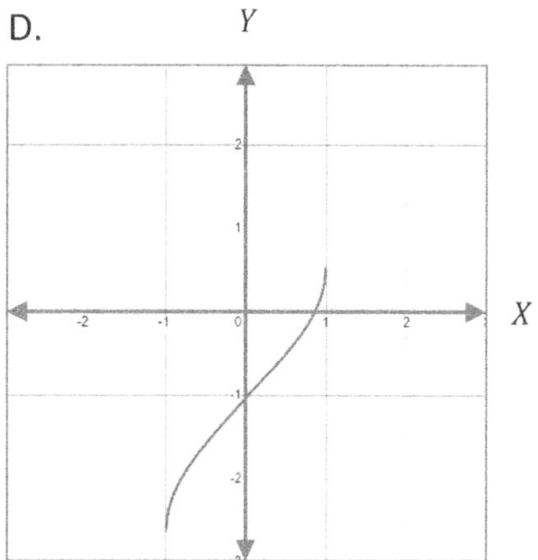

X

18) In right-angled triangle XYZ, with the right angle at Y, if $XY = 3\ cm$ and $XZ - YZ = 1\ cm$, then the value of $(sec\,X + tan\,X)$ is:

A. 3

B. 2

C. $\frac{1}{2}$

D. $\frac{1}{3}$

19) Convert the radian measure $\frac{2\pi}{3}$ to degree measure.

A. $120°$

B. $60°$

C. $90°$

D. $150°$

20) If $sin(A-B)=\frac{\sqrt{3}}{2}$ and $cos(A+B)=\frac{1}{2}$, where $A>B>0$ and $A+B$ is an acute angle, then the value of A is:

A. $\frac{\pi}{12}$

B. $\frac{\pi}{6}$

C. $\frac{\pi}{4}$

D. $\frac{\pi}{3}$

21) Convert 150 degrees to radian.

A. $\frac{\pi}{6}$

B. $\frac{\pi}{12}$

C. $\frac{5\pi}{12}$

D. $\frac{5\pi}{6}$

22) What is the size of angle BAC (Choose the closest angle to the answer).

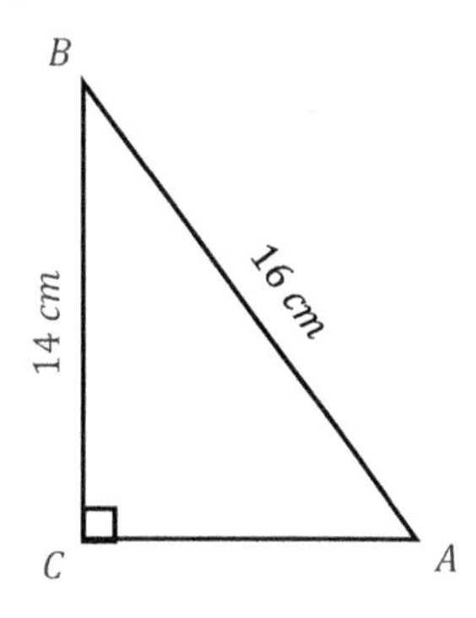

A. 15°

B. 30°

C. 45°

D. 60°

23) The graph of a function $f(x)$ is a transformed trigonometric function. Which of the following represents the function $f(x)$?

A. $f(x) = 3\,cos\left(2\left(x - \frac{\pi}{2}\right)\right) - 1$

B. $f(x) = -3\,cos\left(2\left(x + \frac{\pi}{2}\right)\right) - 1$

C. $f(x) = -3\,sin\left(2\left(x - \frac{\pi}{2}\right)\right) - 1$

D. $f(x) = 3\,sin\left(2\left(x + \frac{\pi}{2}\right)\right) - 1$

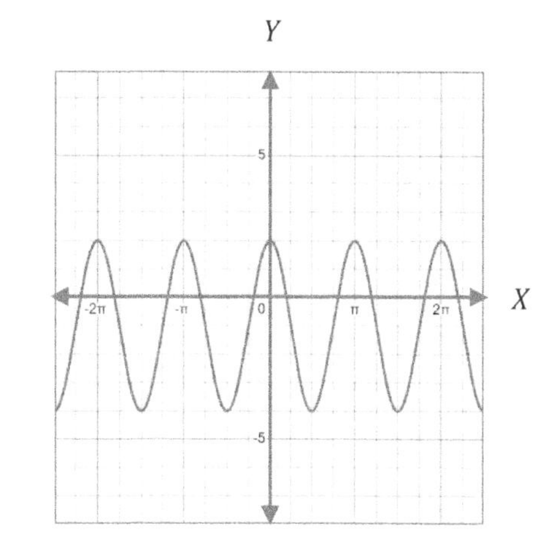

24) If θ is an acute angle and $sin\,\theta = \frac{4}{5}$, then $cos\,\theta =$?

A. $\frac{3}{5}$

B. $\frac{4}{3}$

C. $\frac{3}{4}$

D. $\frac{5}{3}$

25) If $tan\,\theta = \frac{5}{12}$ and $sin\,\theta > 0$, then $cos\,\theta = ?$

A. $\frac{12}{13}$

B. $-\frac{5}{13}$

C. $-\frac{12}{13}$

D. $\frac{13}{12}$

26) The diagram shows a right-angled triangle ABC. (Non-calculator question)

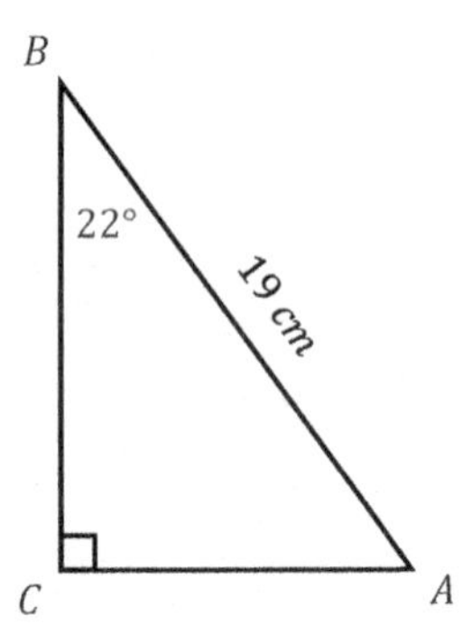

Angle	Sine	Cosine	Tangent
22°	0.375	0.927	0.404
68°	0.927	0.375	2.475

What is the length of BC.

A. 47 cm

B. 17.6 cm

C. 7.7 cm

D. 7.1 cm

27) If $sin\,A = \frac{1}{4}$ is a right triangle and angle A is an acute angle, then what is $cos\,A$?

A. $\frac{1}{4}$

B. $\frac{\sqrt{15}}{4}$

C. $\sqrt{15}$

D. $-\frac{\sqrt{15}}{4}$

28) Find a positive and a negative coterminal angle to angle $125°$.

A. $55°$, $125°$

B. $305°$, $-55°$

C. $-235°$, $485°$

D. $215°$, $35°$

29) If $cot\left(\frac{\pi}{2} - \frac{\varphi}{2}\right) = \sqrt{3}$, the value of $\sin\varphi$ is:

A. 0

B. $\frac{\sqrt{3}}{2}$

C. 1

D. $\frac{2}{\sqrt{3}}$

30) The value of $4(sin\, 45°\, cos\, 15°)$ is:

A. 1

B. $\sqrt{3}$

C. $\sqrt{3} + 1$

D. Not defined.

31) ABC is a right-angled triangle with $\angle A = 90°$. Then the value $sin^2 A + sin^2 B + sin^2 C$ is:

A. 3

B. 2

C. 1

D. 0

32) If $tan\,\theta = \frac{3}{4}$, then the value of $\frac{sin\,\theta + cos\,\theta}{sin\,\theta - cos\,\theta}$ is

A. 7

B. $\frac{1}{7}$

C. $-\frac{1}{7}$

D. -7

33) If $m = 3\cos x - \sin x$ and $n = \cos x + 3\sin x$, then $m^2 + n^2$ is equal to

A. 10

B. 9

C. 4

D. 0

34) If $\cos\alpha \csc 19° = 1$, the value of α is

A. 19°

B. 39°

C. 59°

D. 71°

35) If $\cos C + \cos D = x$, then the value of x is

A. $2\cos\left[\frac{C+D}{2}\right]\cos\left[\frac{C-D}{2}\right]$

B. $2\sin\left[\frac{C+D}{2}\right]\cos\left[\frac{C-D}{2}\right]$

C. $2\cos\left[\frac{C+D}{2}\right]\sin\left[\frac{C-D}{2}\right]$

D. $2\sin\left[\frac{C+D}{2}\right]\sin\left[\frac{D-C}{2}\right]$

36) $1 - \frac{\cos^2 A}{1+\sin A} + \frac{1+\sin A}{\cos A} - \frac{\cos A}{1-\sin A} = ?$

A. $\cos A$

B. 0

C. 1

D. $\sin A$

37) The measures of the angles of a triangle are in the ratio 3: 8: 9. The measures of the angles are

A. 18°, 48°, 114°

B. 30°, 80°, 70°

C. 27°, 72°, 81°

D. 36°, 96°, 48°

38) $ABCD$ is a rectangle of which AC is a diagonal. The value of $(tan^2 \angle ACD + 1)\, sin^2 \angle DAC$ is

A. 0

B. $\frac{1}{2}$

C. 1

D. 2

39) If the cotangent of an angle β is 1, then the tangent of angle β is $\cdots$?

A. 0

B. -1

C. $-\infty$

D. 1

40) The angles of depression of two boats from the top of a lighthouse are $30°$ and $45°$ towards the east. If the boats are 200 meters apart, the height of the lighthouse is:

A. 100 meter

B. $100\sqrt{3}$ meter

C. 200 meter

D. $100(1+\sqrt{3})$ meter

41) If $2(sin^2\theta - cos^2\theta) = -1$, θ is a positive acute angle, then the value of θ is

A. $60°$

B. $45°$

C. $30°$

D. $22.5°$

42) The expression of $\frac{\tan\theta+\sec\theta-1}{\tan\theta-\sec\theta+1}$ is equal to

A. $\frac{\sin\theta+1}{\cos\theta}$

B. $\frac{1-\sin\theta}{\cos\theta}$

C. $\frac{\tan\theta+1}{\sec\theta}$

D. $\frac{\tan\theta-1}{\sec\theta}$

43) If $2\sin\theta - 5\cos\theta = 4$ then the value of $2\cos\theta + 5\sin\theta$ is:

A. $\pm\sqrt{35}$

B. $\pm\sqrt{30}$

C. $\pm\sqrt{13}$

D. $\pm\sqrt{5}$

44) The simplified value of $(\csc x \csc y + \cot x \cot y)^2 - (\csc x \cot y + \cot x \csc y)^2$ is:

A. 1

B. 0

C. -1

D. $\csc^2 x$

45) If $\sec\theta + \cos\theta = 2$, then the value of $\sin^3\theta + \cos^3\theta$ is

A. 8

B. 2

C. 1

D. 0

46) If $\frac{\sin\theta}{A} = \frac{\cos\theta}{B}$, then $\sin\theta + \cos\theta$ is equal to

A. $A + B$

B. $A - B$

C. $\frac{A+B}{\sqrt{A^2+B^2}}$

D. $\frac{A-B}{\sqrt{A^2+B^2}}$

47) If $\csc\theta - \cot\theta = \frac{5}{2}$, the value of $\csc\theta$ is:

A. $\frac{21}{20}$

B. $\frac{23}{20}$

C. $\frac{25}{20}$

D. $\frac{29}{20}$

48) Find the length of the side RT in the triangle below.

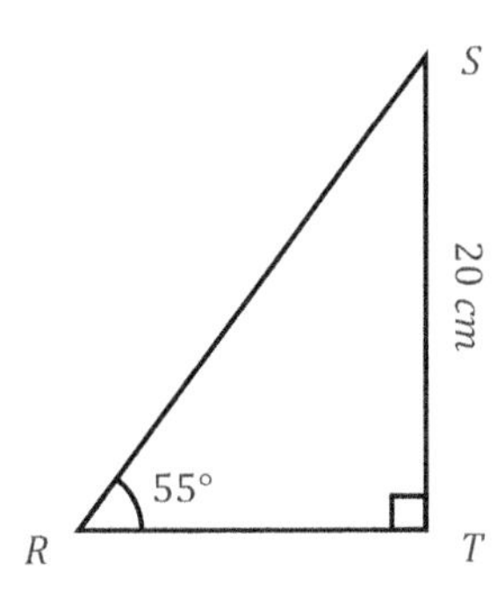

A. 35

B. 24.4

C. 20

D. 14

49) ABC is a right-angled triangle, right angled at B and $\angle A = 45°$ and $AB = 10\ cm$, then the ratio of sides BC and CA is:

A. $\sqrt{2}: 1$

B. $1: \sqrt{2}$

C. $\sqrt{2}: \sqrt{3}$

D. $\sqrt{2}: 3$

50) $\frac{\tan\theta}{1+\cot\theta} - \frac{\cot\theta}{1+\tan\theta}$ is equal to

A. $\tan\theta + \cot\theta + 1$

B. $\tan\theta - \cot\theta + 1$

C. $\tan\theta + \cot\theta - 1$

D. $\tan\theta - \cot\theta - 1$

End of Trigonometry Practice Test 2

Trigonometry Practice Tests Answer Keys

Now, it's time to review your results to see where you went wrong and what areas you need to improve.

Trigonometry Practice Test 1						Trigonometry Practice Test 2					
1	C	21	B	41	C	1	D	21	D	41	C
2	A	22	D	42	B	2	D	22	D	42	A
3	C	23	D	43	B	3	C	23	B	43	C
4	C	24	D	44	D	4	A	24	A	44	A
5	A	25	A	45	C	5	D	25	A	45	C
6	A	26	B	46	C	6	A	26	B	46	C
7	C	27	B	47	B	7	B	27	B	47	D
8	A	28	B	48	C	8	A	28	C	48	D
9	C	29	A	49	D	9	B	29	B	49	B
10	D	30	C	50	B	10	D	30	C	50	C
11	B	31	A	51		11	D	31	B	51	
12	B	32	B	52		12	B	32	D	52	
13	D	33	B	53		13	C	33	A	53	
14	C	34	B	54		14	A	34	D	54	
15	C	35	B	55		15	D	35	A	55	
16	B	36	B	56		16	B	36	D	56	
17	C	37	B	57		17	A	37	C	57	
18	D	38	A	58		18	A	38	C	58	
19	C	39	D	59		19	A	39	D	59	
20	A	40	C	60		20	D	40	D	60	

Trigonometry Practice Tests Answers and Explanations

Trigonometry Practice Tests 1 Explanations

1) Choice C is correct.

Let's rewrite the equation using the reciprocal identities: $5 - \sin^2\theta = \frac{4}{\sin\theta}$. Multiplying both sides by $\sin\theta$, we get: $5\sin\theta - \sin^3\theta = 4$. We can rewrite $\sin^3\theta$ as $(\sin\theta)^3$:

$(\sin\theta)^3 - 5\sin\theta + 4 = 0$

Now, let's solve this cubic equation. We can see that $\theta = 90°$ is one of the solutions. To find the other solutions, we can use numerical methods or approximation techniques.

For $\theta = 0°$: $(\sin 0°)^3 - 5\sin 0° + 4 = 0^3 - 5(0) + 4 \neq 0$

For $\theta = 30°$: $(\sin 30°)^3 - 5\sin 30° + 4 = \left(\frac{1}{2}\right)^3 - 5\left(\frac{1}{2}\right) + 4 = \frac{13}{8} \neq 0$

For $\theta = 45°$: $(\sin 45°)^3 - 5\sin 45° + 4 = 4 = \left(\frac{\sqrt{2}}{2}\right)^3 - 5\left(\frac{\sqrt{2}}{2}\right) + 4 = \frac{16-9\sqrt{2}}{4} \neq 0$

For $\theta = 60°$: $(\sin 60°)^3 - 5\sin 60° + 4 = \left(\frac{\sqrt{3}}{2}\right)^3 - 5\left(\frac{\sqrt{3}}{2}\right) + 4 = \frac{3\sqrt{3}}{8} - \frac{5\sqrt{3}}{2} + 4 = \frac{-17\sqrt{3}}{8} + 4 \neq 0$

For $\theta = 90°$: $(\sin 90°)^3 - 5\sin 90° + 4 = 1 - 5 + 4 = 0$

2) Choice A is correct.

Let's consider the given right-angled triangle PQR. Since angle Q is the right angle, we can apply trigonometric identities to find the values of $\sec P$ and $\tan P$ in terms of the sides of the triangle. Using the Pythagorean theorem, we know that $PQ^2 + QR^2 = PR^2$. Substituting the given values, we have $(7)^2 + QR^2 = (QR + 5)^2$. Simplifying, we obtain $49 + QR^2 = QR^2 + 10QR + 25$. By canceling out the QR^2 terms, we get $49 = 10QR + 25$. Rearranging the equation, we have $10QR = 49 - 25 = 24$. Dividing both sides by 10, we find that $QR = \frac{24}{10} = 2.4$. Now, let's consider the trigonometric functions $\sec P$ and $\tan P$. $\sec P$ is the reciprocal of $\cos P$, and $\tan P$ is the ratio of $\sin P$ to $\cos P$. To find these values, we can use the side lengths of the triangle. Using the given values, we have $\cos P = \frac{PQ}{PR} = \frac{7}{2.4+5} = \frac{7}{7.4} = \frac{70}{74}$. So, the value of $\sec P = \frac{1}{\cos P}$, and $\sec P = \frac{74}{70} = \frac{37}{35}$. On the other hand, we know that $\tan\theta = \frac{\text{The opposite side to the angle}}{\text{The side adjacent to the angle}}$. For the angle P, we have: $\tan\theta = \frac{QR}{PQ}$. Therefore, $\tan P = \frac{2.4}{7} = \frac{12}{35}$. Finally, adding $\sec P + \tan P$, we get $\sec P + \tan P = \frac{37}{35} + \frac{12}{35} = \frac{49}{35} = \frac{7}{5} = 1 + \frac{2}{5}$. Therefore, the correct answer is B, $1 + \frac{2}{5}$.

3) Choice C is correct.

In a regular hexagon, if each side length is a, then the hexagon can indeed be divided into six equilateral triangles, each with a side length of a. In an equilateral triangle, the height h can be calculated using Pythagoras' theorem, which is derived from the fact that the height splits the equilateral triangle into two 30-60-90 triangles. As follows:

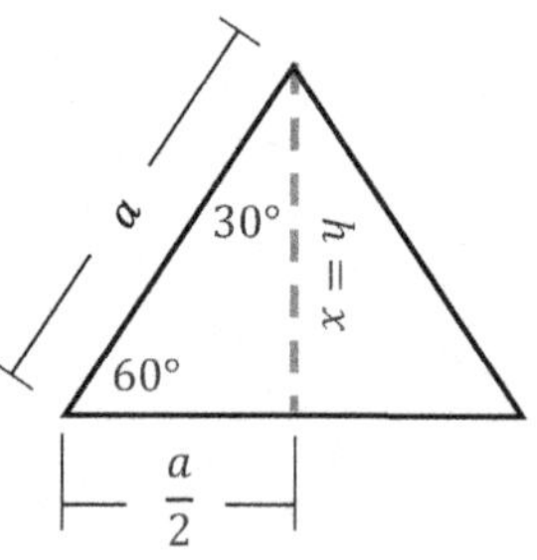

The height $h = x$ can be calculated as follows: $h = \frac{\sqrt{3}}{2}a$.

This is because in an equilateral triangle, the height forms a right angle with the base and divides the base into two segments of equal length $\frac{a}{2}$, creating two 30-60-90 triangles. In such a triangle, the side opposite the 60-degree angle (which is the height in this case) is $\frac{\sqrt{3}}{2}$ times the length of the hypotenuse a. Because,

$$\sin 60° = \frac{h}{a} \rightarrow \frac{\sqrt{3}}{2} = \frac{x}{a} \rightarrow x = \frac{\sqrt{3}}{2}a$$

So, the height of each of the equilateral triangles is $x = \frac{\sqrt{3}}{2}a$.

4) Choice C is correct.

Given $4\sin^2\theta + 3\cos^2\theta = \frac{7}{2}$. We can rewrite the equation as $4\sin^2\theta + 3(1 - \sin^2\theta) = \frac{7}{2}$, using the identity $\cos^2\theta = 1 - \sin^2\theta$ (since $\sin^2\theta + \cos^2\theta = 1$). Solving for $\sin^2\theta$ gives us:

$4\sin^2\theta + 3(1 - \sin^2\theta) = \frac{7}{2} \rightarrow 4\sin^2\theta + 3 - 3\sin^2\theta = \frac{7}{2}$

$$\rightarrow sin^2\theta = \frac{7}{2} - 3$$

$$\rightarrow sin^2\theta = \frac{1}{2}$$

Since $0 < \theta < \frac{\pi}{2}$, $sin\,\theta = \sqrt{\frac{1}{2}} = \frac{1}{\sqrt{2}}$. We know that $tan\,\theta = \frac{sin\,\theta}{cos\,\theta}$. Using the Pythagorean identity $cos^2\theta = 1 - sin^2\theta$, we find that $cos\,\theta = \sqrt{1 - sin^2\theta} = \sqrt{1 - \left(\frac{1}{\sqrt{2}}\right)^2} = \sqrt{1 - \frac{1}{2}} = \frac{1}{\sqrt{2}}$.

Therefore, $tan\,\theta = \frac{sin\,\theta}{cos\,\theta} = \frac{\frac{1}{\sqrt{2}}}{\frac{1}{\sqrt{2}}} = 1$. So, the correct answer is C, 1.

5) Choice A is correct.

In a right triangle ABC with $\angle C = 90°$, we can express $sec\,B$ and $tan\,A$ using the sides of the triangle: $sec\,B = \frac{1}{cos\,B}$. In right triangle ABC, $cos\,B = \frac{adjacent}{hypotenuse} = \frac{y}{x}$.

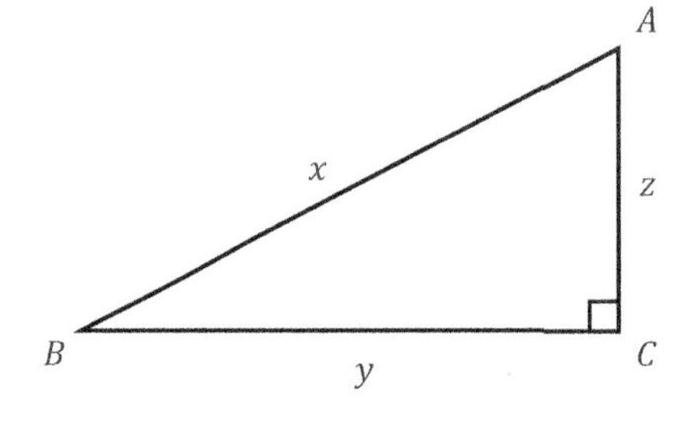

Hence, $sec\,B = \frac{x}{y}$. Similarly, $tan\,A = \frac{opposite}{adjacent} = \frac{y}{z}$ in the triangle. Hence, the value of $(sec\,B \cdot tan\,A) = \left(\frac{x}{y}\right)\left(\frac{y}{z}\right) = \frac{x}{z}$.

6) Choice A is correct.

Since the secant function $sec(x) = \frac{1}{cos(x)}$, rewrite the given function as: $f(x) = 2\,cos(x - \pi)$.

Determine the domain:

The domain of a function is the set of all possible input values (often denoted as x −values) that will give a valid output from a particular function. The cosine function, $cos(x)$, is defined for all real numbers. Thus, the function $2\,cos(x - \pi)$ is also defined for all real numbers since it's just a cosine function that's been scaled and shifted. So, the domain of this function is all real numbers $\mathbb{R}$, or in interval notation, $(-\infty, +\infty)$.

Determine the range:

The range of a function is the set of all possible output values (often denoted as y −values) that are valid for a given input to the function. The cosine function yields all values of y in the interval $[-1,1]$, because the cosine of any angle is always between -1 and 1 inclusive.

Since $f(x) = 2\cos(x-\pi)$, the range of $f(x)$ will be all real numbers in the interval $[-2,2]$ because the function is the cosine function scaled vertically by a factor of 2 as:

$-1 \le \cos(x-\pi) \le 1 \rightarrow -2 \le 2\cos(x-\pi) \le 2$

In summary, the domain of the function $f(x) = \frac{2}{\sec(x-\pi)}$ is all real numbers, and the range is $[-2,2]$.

7) Choice C is correct.

From the given equation $\cot(\alpha-\beta) = 1$, we have that $\alpha - \beta = 45°$ (because $\cot 45° = 1$). From the given equation $\csc(\alpha+\beta) = 2$, we have that $\sin(\alpha+\beta) = \frac{1}{2}$, so $\alpha+\beta = 30°$ or $\alpha+\beta = 150°$ (because $\sin 30° = \frac{1}{2}$ and $\sin 150° = \frac{1}{2}$). Since α and β are both positive, the total of α and β (i.e., $\alpha+\beta$) must be greater than the difference (i.e., $\alpha-\beta$). Therefore, we discard the solution $\alpha+\beta = 30°$ as it would mean $\alpha-\beta > \alpha+\beta$, which is not possible.

Therefore, $\alpha+\beta = 150°$. From this and $\alpha-\beta = 45°$, we can form a system of equations to solve for α:

$$\begin{cases} \alpha+\beta = 150° \\ \alpha-\beta = 45° \end{cases} \rightarrow 2\alpha = 150° + 45° \rightarrow \alpha = \frac{195°}{2} = 97.5°$$

So, the smallest value of α is $97.5°$.

8) Choice A is correct.

The expression, $y = 4\sin^2\alpha + 5\cos^2\alpha$, can be written as follow:

$$4(\sin^2\alpha + \cos^2\alpha) + \cos^2\alpha = 4 + \cos^2\alpha$$

Here, the function $y = 4 + \cos^2\alpha$, will always be greater than or equal to 4. Because the value of the function cosine is $-1 \le \cos\alpha \le 1$, then $0 \le \cos^2\alpha \le 1$.

So, the value of the function $y = 4 + cos^2 \alpha$ is $4 \le 4 + cos^2 \alpha \le 5 \to 4 \le y \le 5$. Therefore, the minimum value is 4 (Choice A).

9) Choice C is correct.

According to the trigonometric circle and $tan\,\theta = \frac{opposite}{adjacent}$, and since, $sin\,\theta < 0$ and $tan\,\theta > 0$, therefore, $cos\,\theta < 0$. Considering, $tan\,\theta = \frac{5}{12}$, then:

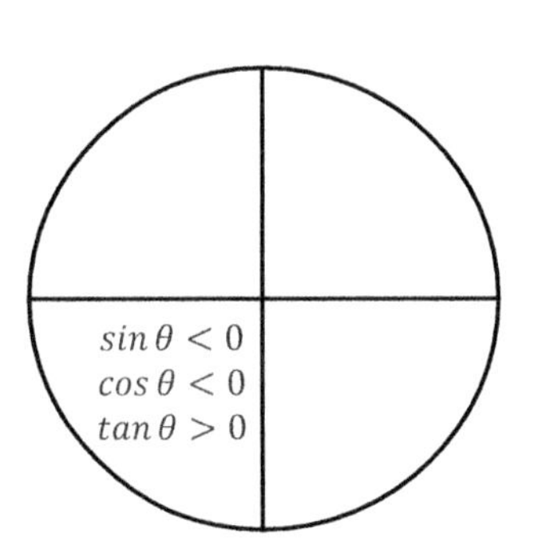

$c = \sqrt{5^2 + 12^2} = \sqrt{25 + 144} = \sqrt{169} = 13$,

$$cos\,\theta = \frac{adjacent}{hypotenuse} \to cos\,\theta = -\frac{12}{13}$$

10) Choice D is correct.

The value of $cos\,240° = -\,cos\,60°$ and $cos\,300° = cos(360 - 300)° = cos\,60°$. So,

$cos^2\,240° + cos^2\,300° = (-\,cos\,60°)^2 + (cos\,60°)^2 = \left(-\frac{1}{2}\right)^2 + \left(\frac{1}{2}\right)^2 = \frac{1}{2}$

Hence, the correct option is D, $\frac{1}{2}$.

11) Choice B is correct.

We can use the addition and subtraction formula for sine and cosine to solve this problem.

$cos(60° + \theta) = cos\,60°\,cos\,\theta - sin\,60°\,sin\,\theta = \left(\frac{1}{2}\right) cos\,\theta - \left(\frac{\sqrt{3}}{2}\right) sin\,\theta$

$sin(30° - \theta) = sin\,30°\,cos\,\theta - cos\,30°\,sin\,\theta = \left(\frac{1}{2}\right) cos\,\theta - \left(\frac{\sqrt{3}}{2}\right) sin\,\theta$

Subtracting these two expressions, we obtain:

$$\begin{aligned} cos(60° + \theta) - sin(60° - \theta) &= \left(\frac{1}{2}\right) cos\,\theta - \left(\frac{\sqrt{3}}{2}\right) sin\,\theta - \left[\left(\frac{1}{2}\right) cos\,\theta - \left(\frac{\sqrt{3}}{2}\right) sin\,\theta\right] \\ &= \left(\frac{1}{2}\right) cos\,\theta - \left(\frac{\sqrt{3}}{2}\right) sin\,\theta - \left(\frac{1}{2}\right) cos\,\theta + \left(\frac{\sqrt{3}}{2}\right) sin\,\theta \\ &= 0 \end{aligned}$$

So, the answer is B, 0.

12) Choice B is correct.

We're looking for a sine function since the graph appears to start at its midpoint and moves upwards, indicative of the sine function. The graph has an amplitude of 2 which tells us that the coefficient in front of the sine function is 2. The period of the graph is 2π which is standard for sine and cosine functions, so we don't need to adjust for period in the function. The graph is shifted $\frac{\pi}{2}$ units to the right, indicating a phase shift. The phase shift in the sine function is opposite to what it looks like. Hence, the function is $y = 2\,sin\left(x - \frac{\pi}{2}\right)$. The graph is also shifted up by 1 unit. This tells us that we're dealing with a vertical shift. This adds +1 outside the function. So, the equation of the graph is $y = 2\,sin\left(x - \frac{\pi}{2}\right) + 1$.

Therefore, the correct answer is: B. $y = 2\,sin\left(x - \frac{\pi}{2}\right) + 1$.

13) Choice D is correct.

Let's go through the options one by one:

A. $\frac{\pi}{3}$: $cos^2\left(\frac{\pi}{3}\right) = \left(\frac{1}{2}\right)^2 = \frac{1}{4}$ and $1 - \left(\frac{\pi}{3}\right)^2 = 1 - \frac{\pi^2}{9} \approx -0.097$.

B. $\frac{\pi}{4}$: $cos^2\left(\frac{\pi}{4}\right) = \left(\frac{\sqrt{2}}{2}\right)^2 = \frac{1}{2}$ and $1 - \left(\frac{\pi}{4}\right)^2 = 1 - \frac{\pi^2}{16} \approx 0.38$.

C. 1: $cos^2(1) = (cos(1))^2 \approx 0.292$ and $1 - 1^2 = 1 - 1 = 0$.

D. 0: $cos^2(0) = 1^2 = 1$ and $1 - 0^2 = 1$.

So, we can see that only for $x = 0$ does the equation $cos^2(x) = 1 - x^2$ hold true. Therefore, the correct answer is D. 0.

14) Choice C is correct.

We know that $cos\,\theta = \frac{\sqrt{2}}{2}$ implies $\theta = 45°$. So, $cot(45° + 15°) = cot\,60° = \frac{\sqrt{3}}{3}$ (Or $\frac{1}{\sqrt{3}}$).

Hence, the correct option is C, $\frac{1}{\sqrt{3}}$.

15) Choice C is correct.

Let's start by expressing $sec\,\theta - tan\,\theta$ in terms of sine and cosine functions: $sec\,\theta = \frac{1}{cos\,\theta}$ and $tan\,\theta = \frac{sin\,\theta}{cos\,\theta}$. So, the given equation $sec\,\theta - tan\,\theta = \sqrt{2}$ becomes: $\frac{1}{cos\,\theta} - \frac{sin\,\theta}{cos\,\theta} = \sqrt{2}$. Simplify this to get: $\frac{1 - sin\,\theta}{cos\,\theta} = \sqrt{2}$. Multiply both sides by $cos\,\theta$ to get: $1 - sin\,\theta = \sqrt{2}\,cos\,\theta$. Square both sides to eliminate the square root: $1 - 2\,sin\,\theta + sin^2\,\theta = 2\,cos^2\,\theta$.

We can use the identity $sin^2\theta + cos^2\theta = 1$, which gives $cos^2\theta = 1 - sin^2\theta$, to rewrite the equation: $1 - 2\,sin\,\theta + sin^2\theta = 2 - 2\,sin^2\theta$. Rearrange to get: $3\,sin^2\theta - 2\,sin\,\theta - 1 = 0$.

This equation is a quadratic equation in $sin\,\theta$. Let's solve for $sin\,\theta$ using the quadratic formula,

$sin\,\theta = \frac{-(-2)\pm\sqrt{(-2)^2-4(3)(-1)}}{2\times3} = \frac{2\pm\sqrt{4+12}}{6} = \frac{2\pm4}{6}$. Solving this gives two solutions: $sin\,\theta = 1$ and $sin\,\theta = -\frac{1}{3}$. But $-\frac{1}{3}$ is not a valid solution as $sin\,\theta$ ranges from -1 to 1 and θ ranges from $0°$ to $90°$. So, the only valid solution is $sin(\theta) = 1$. For θ in the first quadrant ($0° \leq \theta \leq 90°$), this happens at $\theta = 90°$.

Then we need to calculate $tan\,2\theta$. When $\theta = 90°$, $2\theta = 180°$, then $tan\,180° = 0$. So, the answer is C.

16) Choice B is correct.

For this purpose, first consider the graph of the secant function. We could then evaluate these values as follows:

The distance between the two parts of the graph in the secant function is 2 (The horizontal box specified in the graph). a is the amplitude of the function. Since in the given graph this difference is 4 units, so the amplitude is half of this difference. That is, $a = 2$.

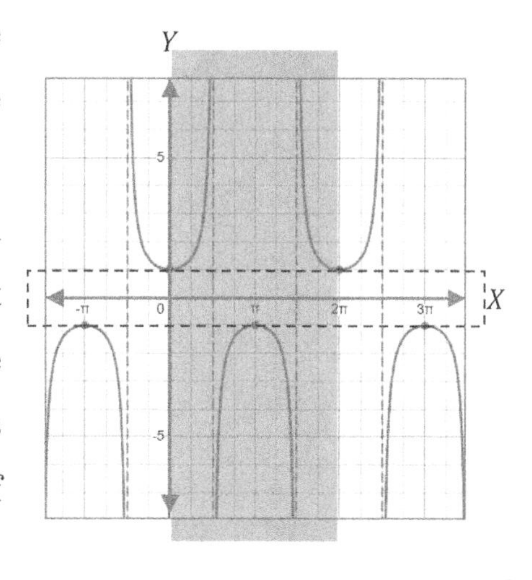

b determines the period of the function (period $= \frac{2\pi}{b}$). The vertical box shown in the secant graph, which is 2π units on the $x-$axis and corresponds to this box on the graph of the content of the question, is 3 units. So, we get $4 = \frac{2\pi}{b} \rightarrow b = \frac{\pi}{2}$.

c, which equals 1 here, represents the vertical shift of the function. Therefore our function should be shifted up by 1 unit. Because, the middle horizontal line between the two parts of the secant graph is the $x-$axis. In the graph of problem, the corresponding horizontal line is shifted up by one unit. So, $d = +1$. We would then compare this to the provided graph. If the graph fits these characteristics, then option B is the correct answer.

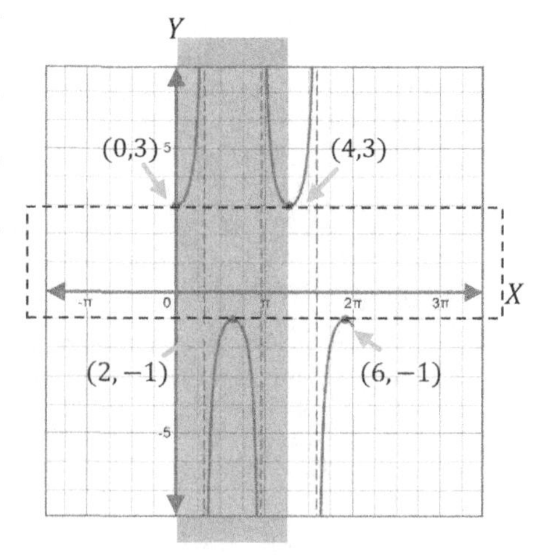

17) Choice C is correct.

The question can be solved by understanding trigonometric relationships. The angle in question is the one that the line connecting the child's hand (from where the stone will be thrown) and the kite makes with the horizontal.

We are essentially interested in finding the angle of elevation.

We know the opposite side (height of the kite - height of the child) and the adjacent side (distance of the child from the tree). So, we can use the tangent of the angle, defined as the ratio of the opposite side to the adjacent side.

Let's denote the height of the tree as "h_1" ($20\ ft$), the height of the child as "h_2" ($4\ ft$), and the distance of the child from the tree as "d" ($5\ ft$).

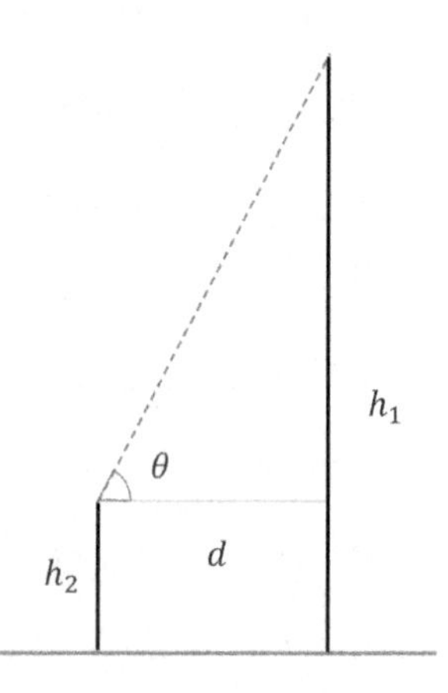

Then, the tangent of the angle θ is as follow:

$$tan\,\theta = \frac{h_1 - h_2}{d} = \frac{20 - 4}{5} = \frac{16}{5} = 3.2$$

To find the angle, we take the arctan (inverse tangent) of 3.2. Using a calculator, $arctan(3.2)$ is approximately $72.65°$. Therefore, the closest option is (C) $72°$, but it's not exactly the correct answer.

18) Choice D is correct.

To find the value of θ based on the given equation, we can use trigonometric identities and algebraic manipulation. Given the equation: $5\,cos^2(\theta) + sin^2(\theta) = 4$. We can use the identity $sin^2(\theta) + cos^2(\theta) = 1$ to rewrite the equation: $5(1 - sin^2(\theta)) + sin^2(\theta) = 4$. Simplifying further: $5 - 5\,sin^2(\theta) + sin^2(\theta) = 4$. Combining like terms: $5 - 4\,sin^2(\theta) = 4$. Rearranging the equation: $4\,sin^2(\theta) = 5 - 4 \rightarrow 4\,sin^2(\theta) = 1$. Dividing both sides by 4: $sin^2(\theta) = \frac{1}{4}$. Taking the square root of both sides: $sin(\theta) = \pm\frac{1}{2}$. Since θ is a positive acute angle, $sin(\theta)$ will be positive. Therefore: $sin(\theta) = \frac{1}{2}$. Now, we need to find the corresponding angle θ. We can determine that: $\theta = 30°$. Therefore, the value of θ is $30°$. The choice D is the correct answer.

19) Choice C is correct.

We convert the angle of $\angle ACB = \frac{\pi}{4}$ to degrees. The sum of the angles of a triangle is $180°$. So, $\angle BAC = 180° - 85° - 45° = 50°$. Converting to radians, we get $\angle BAC = 50° \times \frac{\pi}{180°} = \frac{5\pi}{18}$ radians. Hence, the correct option is C, $\frac{5\pi}{18}$ radian.

20) Choice A is correct.

Recall that $sec\,\theta = \frac{1}{cos\,\theta}$ and $sin(90 - \theta) = cos\,\theta$. Hence,

$$sec\,15° - sin\,75° = \frac{1}{cos\,15°} - sin(90° - 15)$$
$$= \frac{1}{cos\,15°} - cos\,15°$$
$$= \frac{1 - cos^2\,15°}{cos\,15°}$$

Substitute given $cos\,15° = x$ into the expression $\frac{1-cos^2\,15°}{cos\,15°}$, we get: $\frac{1-(x)^2}{x} = \frac{1-x^2}{x}$.

Therefore, the correct option is A, $\frac{1-x^2}{x}$.

21) Choice B is correct.

First, it is worth noting that $cos(\theta + 180°) = -\,cos(\theta)$ because the cosine function is negative in the second and third quadrants (which $\varphi + 180°$ falls into if φ is an acute angle). Given that $cos(\varphi + 180°) = -\frac{\sqrt{3}}{2}$, then $-cos\,\varphi = -\frac{\sqrt{3}}{2}$, and $cos\,\varphi = \frac{\sqrt{3}}{2}$. We know that this is the cosine of an angle of $\frac{\pi}{6}$ radians (or 30°) in the first quadrant (where cosine is positive). Therefore, the value of φ is $\frac{\pi}{6}$ radian. So, the answer is B, $\frac{\pi}{6}$ radian.

22) Choice D is correct.

Given $\alpha + \beta = 120°$ and $\alpha:\beta = 1:3$, we can solve for α and β first. Since $\alpha:\beta = 1:3$, let $\alpha = x$ and $\beta = 3x$. Then, from the given $\alpha + \beta = 120°$, we get:

$$x + 3x = 120° \rightarrow 4x = 120° \rightarrow x = 30°$$

So, $\alpha = 30°$ and $\beta = 3 \times 30° = 90°$.

Now, we need to find the ratio of $sin\,\beta$ to $sin\,\alpha$: $\frac{sin\,\beta}{sin\,\alpha} = \frac{sin\,90°}{sin\,30°}$. $sin\,90°$ is 1 and $sin\,30°$ is $\frac{1}{2}$, therefore the ratio is: $\frac{sin\,\beta}{sin\,\alpha} = \frac{1}{\frac{1}{2}} = \frac{2}{1}$. The option D is the correct answer.

23) Choice D is correct.

We have $r\,sin\,\theta = \sqrt{3}$ and $r\,cos\,\theta = 3$. Dividing the two equations, we get $tan\,\theta = \frac{\sqrt{3}}{3}$, which gives $\theta = 30°$. Also, $r\,cos\,30° = 3 \rightarrow \frac{\sqrt{3}}{2}r = 3 \rightarrow r = 2\sqrt{3}$. Hence, the correct option is D, $r = 2\sqrt{3}$, $\theta = 30°$.

24) Choice D is correct.

We have $sin\left(\frac{A+B}{2}\right) = \frac{1}{2}$. This implies $\frac{A+B}{2} = 30°$ or $A + B = 60°$. Hence $C = 120°$ (Because $A + B + C = 180°$), and $sin\left(\frac{C}{2}\right) = sin\left(\frac{120°}{2}\right) = sin(60°) = \frac{\sqrt{3}}{2}$. Hence, the correct option is D, $\frac{\sqrt{3}}{2}$.

25) Choice A is correct.

To find AC, use sine B. Then: $sin\,\theta = \frac{opposite}{hypotenuse}$.

$sin\,40° = \frac{AC}{6} \rightarrow 6 \times sin\,40° = AC$.

Now use a calculator to find: $sin\,40°$. $sin\,40° \approx 0.643 \rightarrow AC = 3.858 \approx 3.86$.

26) Choice B is correct.

Given the angles and the time it takes for the angle of depression to change; we can use the tangent of the angles of depression to determine the time it will take for the boat to reach the beach.

$$\begin{matrix} h = (x+8)\,tan\,25^\circ \\ h = x\,tan\,50^\circ \end{matrix} \rightarrow x\,tan\,50^\circ = (x+8)\,tan\,25^\circ \rightarrow x = \frac{8\,tan\,25^\circ}{tan\,50^\circ - tan\,25^\circ} \approx 5$$

Therefore, the correct option is B, 5 minutes.

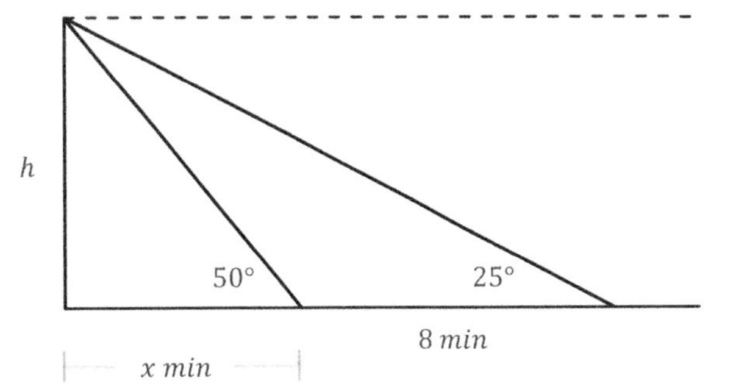

27) Choice B is correct.

The given equation, $cos\,x \cdot cos\,y + sin\,x \cdot sin\,y = 1$, can be rewritten using the cosine of the difference of two angles identity, i.e., $cos(x-y) = cos\,x \cdot cos\,y + sin\,x \cdot sin\,y$. So, we have $cos(x-y) = 1$. The equation $cos(x-y) = 1$ has solutions when $x - y$ equals to 0 or any multiple of 2π (because the cosine of 0 or any multiple of 2π is 1). Let's assume $x - y = 0$ (the simplest solution). This gives us $x = y$. Substitute $y = x$ into the second equation to find $sin\,x - sin\,y = sin\,x - sin\,x = 0$.

28) Choice B is correct.

We know that: $sin^2\,a + cos^2\,a = 1$. This means that:

$x + sin^2\,a + cos^2\,a = 3 \rightarrow x + 1 = 3 \rightarrow x = 2$.

29) Choice A is correct.

Let's check each option.

For θ in $(0^\circ, 90^\circ)$, $0 < sin\,\theta < 1$, so it's clear that $sin\,\theta$ is always greater than $sin^2\,\theta$. Therefore, the correct answer is A, $sin\,\theta > sin^2\,\theta$.

30) Choice C is correct.

In a triangle ABC, if $\tan A = \cot B$, it means that angles A and B are complementary (because the tangent of an angle is equal to the cotangent of its complementary angle, and $\cot(90° - \theta) = \tan\theta$). In a triangle, the sum of the angles is 180 degrees, therefore, if A and B are complementary (sum to 90 degrees), then angle C must be 90 degrees. The $\sin$ of 90 degree is 1, so the correct answer is C, 1.

31) Choice A is correct.

Let's consider the given right-angled triangle LMN. Since angle N is 90°, we know that $\angle L + \angle M = 90°$. Given that $LN: NM = 3: 1$, we can assign values to the sides of the triangle. Let $LN = 3x$ and $NM = x$.

Using the Pythagorean theorem, we have $LM^2 = LN^2 + NM^2 = (3x)^2 + x^2 = 9x^2 + x^2 = 10x^2$. Taking the square root of both sides, we have $LM = x\sqrt{10}$. Now, let's consider the trigonometric functions $\sin L$ and $\cot M$. $\sin L$ is the ratio of the length of the side opposite angle L to the hypotenuse, and $\cot M$ is the reciprocal of the tangent of angle M.

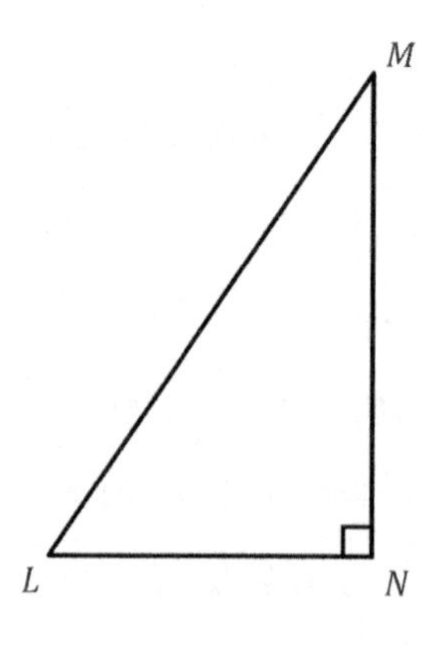

To find these values, we can use the side lengths of the triangle. Using the given values, we have $\sin L = \frac{NM}{LM} = \frac{x}{x\sqrt{10}} = \frac{\sqrt{10}}{10}$. For $\cot M$, we can find the tangent of angle M by using the side lengths of the triangle. The tangent of M is given by the ratio of the side opposite M to the side adjacent to M. Therefore, $\tan M = \frac{LN}{NM} = \frac{3x}{x} = 3$. Taking the reciprocal of $\tan M$, we have $\cot M = \frac{1}{\tan M} = \frac{1}{3}$. Finally, adding $\sin L + \cot M$, we get $\sin L + \cot M = \frac{\sqrt{10}}{10} + \frac{1}{3}$. Finding the common denominator, we have $\frac{3\sqrt{10}+10}{30}$. Therefore, the correct answer is $\frac{3\sqrt{10}+10}{30}$ (Option A).

32) Choice B is correct.

In a right triangle ABC, where $\angle C = 90°$, $AB = 16\ cm$, and $\angle B = 20°$, we can calculate the length of the side BC using the cosine function. The cosine of an angle in a right triangle is the ratio of the length of the side adjacent to the angle to the length of the hypotenuse. Here, the side BC is adjacent to $\angle B$ and AB is the hypotenuse. Therefore, rearranging the formula, we can express BC as follows: $BC = cos(B) \times AB$. Plugging in the values:

$$BC = cos\,20° \times 16\ cm \approx 0.9397 \times 16\ cm \approx 15.03\ cm$$

So, the length of side BC is approximately 15 cm.

33) Choice B is correct.

We know that $tan\,45° = 1$, $sin\,60° = \frac{\sqrt{3}}{2}$, and $csc\,60° = \frac{2}{\sqrt{3}}$. Substituting these values into the given equation, we get:

$$x \times (1) + \frac{\sqrt{3}}{2} = \frac{2}{\sqrt{3}} \rightarrow x + \frac{\sqrt{3}}{2} = \frac{2}{\sqrt{3}}$$

$$\rightarrow x = \frac{2}{\sqrt{3}} - \frac{\sqrt{3}}{2}$$

$$\rightarrow x = \frac{\sqrt{3}}{6}$$

So, the value of $(x^2 + 1)$ is $\left(\frac{\sqrt{3}}{6}\right)^2 + 1 = \frac{3}{36} + 1 = 1 + \frac{1}{12} = \frac{13}{12}$.

34) Choice B is correct.

Given that $tan\,\theta = \frac{3}{4}$, we know that $sin\,\theta = \frac{3}{5}$ and $cos\,\theta = \frac{4}{5}$ by using the Pythagorean identity (because $tan\,\theta = \frac{sin\,\theta}{cos\,\theta}$ and $sin^2\,\theta + cos^2\,\theta = 1$). The given expression is $\frac{\sqrt{1-sin\theta}}{\sqrt{1+sin\theta}}$. Substituting the value of $sin\,\theta$ into this, we get:

$$\frac{\sqrt{1-sin\,\theta}}{\sqrt{1+sin\,\theta}} = \frac{\sqrt{1-\frac{3}{5}}}{\sqrt{1+\frac{3}{5}}} = \frac{\sqrt{\frac{2}{5}}}{\sqrt{\frac{8}{5}}} = \sqrt{\frac{2}{8}} = \sqrt{\frac{1}{4}} = \frac{1}{2}$$

So, the correct answer is B, $\frac{1}{2}$.

35) Choice B is correct.

We know that in a 45-45-90 triangle, the legs are of equal length, and each is $\frac{\sqrt{2}}{2}$ (or $\frac{1}{\sqrt{2}}$) times as long as the hypotenuse. Because in a right-angled triangle for each of the non-right angles, we have: $\sin\theta = \frac{opposite}{hypotenuse}$ (Or $\cos\theta = \frac{adjacent}{hypotenuse}$). Therefore, for the angle 45 degree, we get: $\sin 45° = \frac{opposite}{hypotenuse}$ (Or $\cos 45° = \frac{adjacent}{hypotenuse}$). Given that the base (hypotenuse in this case) is $14\sqrt{2}\ cm$, The length of each of the other sides becomes,

$\frac{\sqrt{2}}{2} = \frac{x}{base} \rightarrow \frac{\sqrt{2}}{2} = \frac{x}{14\sqrt{2}} \rightarrow x = \frac{\sqrt{2}}{2} \times 14\sqrt{2} = 14.$

The altitude (which is also a leg of the right-angled triangle AHC in the figure) will be $\sin\angle ACH = \frac{7\sqrt{2}\ cm}{14\ cm} \rightarrow \sin 45° \times 14\ cm = 7\sqrt{2} \rightarrow \frac{\sqrt{2}}{2} \times 14\ cm = 7\sqrt{2}\ cm.$

Therefore, the correct option is B, $7\sqrt{2}\ cm$.

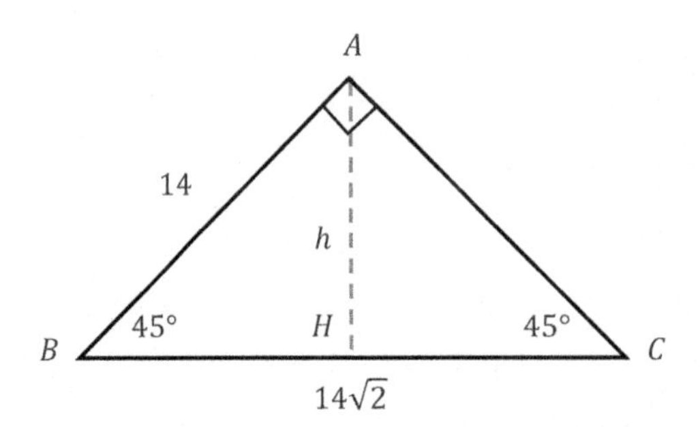

36) Choice B is correct.

Let's denote $y = x - \frac{1}{x}$. Squaring both sides, we get $y^2 = x^2 - 2 + \frac{1}{x^2}$. Substitute $y^2 + 2$ for $x^2 + \frac{1}{x^2}$ in the given equation: $2\cos\left(\frac{\pi x}{3}\right) = y^2 + 2$. Solving for y^2, we get $y^2 = 2\cos\left(\frac{\pi x}{3}\right) - 2$. Remember that for any angle φ, $-1 \le \cos\varphi \le 1$. Therefore, $-1 \le \cos\left(\frac{\pi x}{3}\right) \le 1$, then $-2 \le 2\cos\left(\frac{\pi x}{3}\right) \le 2$, and $-2 \le y^2 + 2 \le 2 \rightarrow -4 \le y^2 \le 0$. Since y^2 is nonnegative, it must be that $y^2 = 0$. Therefore, $y = 0$. In other words, the value of $\left(x + \frac{1}{x}\right)$ is 0, so the answer is B, 0.

37) Choice B is correct.

We can use the tangent of the angles of depression to find the height of the other post. Let's denote the height of the other post as "h".

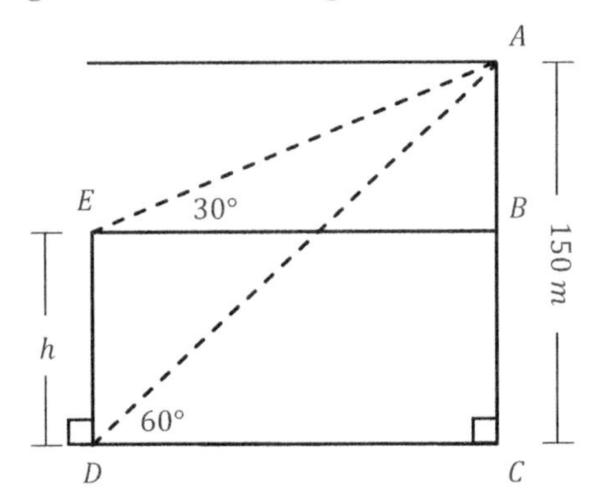

Since $tan(60°) = \frac{150}{DC}$, we get $DC = \frac{150}{tan(60°)} = \frac{150}{\sqrt{3}}$ meters. However, this is the distance between two posts. To determine the height h, we calculate the tangent of 30 degrees. We have:

$$tan\,30° = \frac{AB}{BE} = \frac{150-h}{DC} \rightarrow h = 150 - DC \times tan\,30° \rightarrow h = 150 - \frac{150}{\sqrt{3}} \times \frac{\sqrt{3}}{3} = 100$$

38) Choice A is correct.

The sequence consists of two interleaved arithmetic sequences. The first sequence is made of coefficients of $tan\,45°$ and begins at 1, increases by 2, and ends at 23. The second sequence is made of coefficients of $cos^2\,30°$, begins at 2, increases by 2, and ends at 24. Now, $tan\,45° = 1$ and $cos^2\,30° = \left(\frac{\sqrt{3}}{2}\right)^2 = \frac{3}{4}$.

Let's calculate the sum for each sequence separately.

The first sequence (for $tan\,45°$) has 12 terms. Its sum can be calculated using the formula for the sum of an arithmetic sequence: $\frac{n}{2}(a_1 + a_n)$, where n is the number of terms, a_1 and a_n are the first and nth terms of the sequence. So, $sum_1 = \frac{12}{2}(1+23) = 6 \times 24 = 144$

The second sequence (for $cos^2\,30°$) also has 12 terms. So, $sum_2 = \frac{12}{2}(2+24) = 6 \times 26 = 156$

However, since the terms in this sequence are multiplied by $cos^2 30° = \frac{3}{4}$, we multiply this sum by $\frac{3}{4}$. Therefore, the adjusted $sum_2 = 156\left(\frac{3}{4}\right) = 117$.

Now, let's add the sums together: $sum = sum_1 + sum_2 = 144 + 117 = 261$. Finally, this sum is multiplied by the initial coefficient 126: $\text{total} = 261 \times 126 = 32{,}886$.

So, the value of the expression is 32,886, which is an integer but not a perfect square. Therefore, the answer is A. an integer but not a perfect square.

39) Choice D is correct.

The value of $cos\ 30° = \frac{\sqrt{3}}{2}$.

40) Choice C is correct.

Let's denote the two angles as angle A and angle B. We know that the sum of two angles is 120°, so we have: $A + B = 120$. The difference between the angles is $\frac{\pi}{6}$. To convert it to degrees, we multiply by $\frac{180}{\pi}$: $A - B = \frac{\pi}{6} \times \frac{180}{\pi} = 30°$.

Now, we have a system of equations:

$$\begin{cases} A + B = 120° \\ A - B = 30° \end{cases}$$

Solving this system of equations, we can add the two equations to eliminate B:

$$2A = 150° \rightarrow A = 75°$$

Substituting the value of A back into one of the original equations, we find:

$$75° + B = 120° \rightarrow B = 45°$$

Therefore, the values of the angles are $A = 75°$ and $B = 45°$. The correct answer is C: 45°, 75°.

41) Choice C is correct.

To find the value of x, use the cosine on the angle x:

$$cos\ \theta = \frac{adjacent}{hypotenuse} \rightarrow cos\ x = \frac{10}{14} = \frac{5}{7}$$

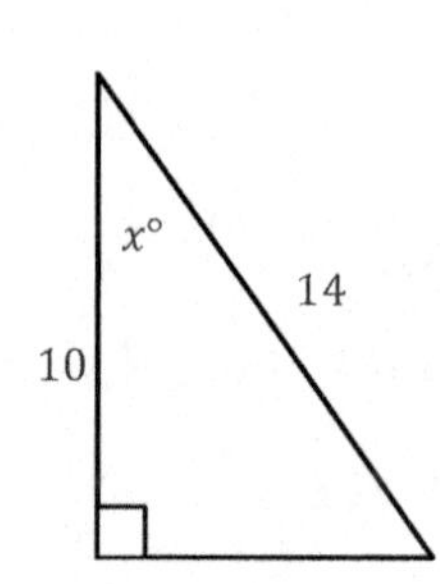

Use a calculator to find inverse cosine:

$cos^{-1}\left(\frac{5}{7}\right) = 44.42° \approx 44°$

Which means that: $x = 44$.

42) Choice B is correct.

The sum of two supplementary angles is 180 degrees. Then: $(2x - 6) + (x + 3) = 180$.

Simplify and solve for x:

$(2x - 6) + (x + 3) = 180 \rightarrow 3x - 3 = 180 \rightarrow 3x = 183 \rightarrow x = 61$.

43) Choice B is correct.

To solve for the side AC, we need to use the sine of angle B. Then:

$sin\,\theta = \frac{opposite}{hypotenuse}$, $sin\,50° = \frac{AC}{6} \rightarrow 6 \times sin\,50° = AC$.

Now use a calculator to find sine of 50°. $sin\,50° \approx 0.766$.

$AC = 6 \times 0.766 = 4.596$, rounding to the nearest tenth: $4.596 \approx 4.6$.

44) Choice D is correct.

Let's first simplify both sides of the equation. We know that $tan\,30° = \frac{\sqrt{3}}{3}$, and $sec\,60° = 2$. So, we can write the given equation $x\,tan\,30° = y\,sec\,60°$ as $x\frac{\sqrt{3}}{3} = 2y$, or equivalently $\frac{x}{y} = 2\sqrt{3}$. Now, let's calculate $\frac{x^4}{y^4}$, which is equal to $\frac{x^4}{y^4} = \left(\frac{x}{y}\right)^4 = \left(2\sqrt{3}\right)^4 = 16 \times 9 = 144 = 12^2$.

45) Choice C is correct.

Since $tan\,\theta = \frac{opposite}{adjacent}$, we have the following: $tan\frac{2\pi}{3} = \frac{sin\frac{2\pi}{3}}{cos\frac{2\pi}{3}} = \frac{\frac{\sqrt{3}}{2}}{-\frac{1}{2}} = -\sqrt{3}$.

46) Choice C is correct.

The given equation is in quadratic form. To find the possible solutions for $sin\,\theta$, we first solve the quadratic equation. The equation $2\,sin^2\,\theta + sin\,\theta - 1 = 0$ can be factored into $(sin\,\theta + 1)(2\,sin\,\theta - 1) = 0$. Setting each factor equal to zero gives us:

$sin\,\theta + 1 = 0 \rightarrow sin\,\theta = -1$

$2\,sin\,\theta - 1 = 0 \rightarrow sin\,\theta = \frac{1}{2}$

The range of the sine function is $-1 \leq sin\,\theta \leq 1$, so $sin\,\theta = -1$ is true for $\theta = 270°$, and $sin\,\theta = \frac{1}{2}$ is true for $\theta = 30°$, $120°$. Therefore, the option C ($\theta = 30°$) is the correct answer.

47) Choice B is correct.

Since D divides BC in the ratio $1:2$, we can define $BD = x$ and $DC = 2x$. Using the Law of Sines in triangles ACD and ABD, we have: $\frac{sin\,\angle CAD}{DC} = \frac{sin\,\angle C}{AD}$ and $\frac{sin\,\angle BAD}{BD} = \frac{sin\,\angle B}{AD}$. By substituting $BD = x$, $DC = 2x$, $\angle B = \frac{\pi}{6}$ and $\angle C = \frac{\pi}{3}$, we have: $\frac{sin\,\angle CAD}{2x} = \frac{\sqrt{3}}{2AD}$ and $\frac{sin\,\angle BAD}{x} = \frac{1}{2AD}$. By solving these two equations, we get:

$$\begin{cases} \frac{sin\,\angle CAD}{2x} = \frac{\sqrt{3}}{2AD} \\ \frac{sin\,\angle BAD}{x} = \frac{1}{2AD} \end{cases} \rightarrow \begin{matrix} AD = \frac{x\sqrt{3}}{sin\,\angle CAD} \\ AD = \frac{x}{2\,sin\,\angle BAD} \end{matrix} \rightarrow \frac{x\sqrt{3}}{sin\,\angle CAD} = \frac{x}{2\,sin\,\angle BAD} \rightarrow \frac{sin\,\angle BAD}{sin\,\angle CAD} = \frac{1}{2\sqrt{3}}$$

So, the answer is B, $\frac{1}{2\sqrt{3}}$.

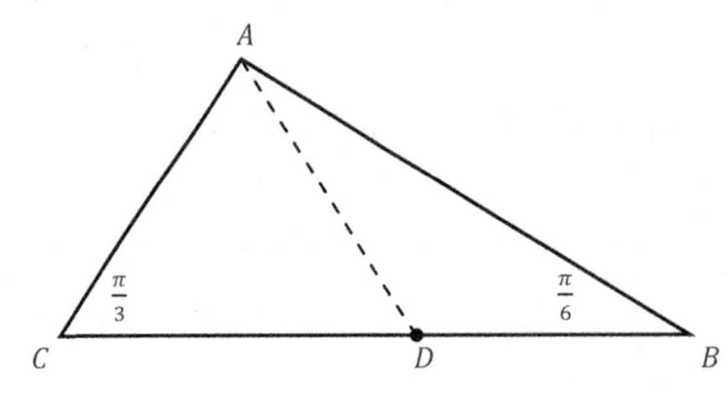

48) Choice C is correct.

We know that $sin\left(\frac{11\pi}{4}\right) = sin\left(\frac{11\pi}{4} - 2\pi\right) = sin\left(\frac{3\pi}{4}\right) = sin\left(\frac{\pi}{4}\right) = \frac{\sqrt{2}}{2}$. Hence, the correct option is C, $\frac{1}{\sqrt{2}}$.

49) Choice D is correct.

According to the contents of the given diagram and those two triangles MNP and NPO are common on the NP side. We evaluate the tangent of the angle 60 degrees for triangle MNP and the cosine of angle x for the triangle NPO. We get:

For ΔMNP: $tan\,\angle NMP = \frac{NP}{MN} \rightarrow NP = MN \times tan\,60° \rightarrow NP = 6\sqrt{3}$

For ΔNPO: $cos\,\angle ONP = \frac{NP}{NO} \rightarrow NP = N0 \times cos\,x \rightarrow NP = 12\,cos\,x$

Next, we have: $12\,cos\,x = 6\sqrt{3}$, then $cos\,x = \frac{\sqrt{3}}{2}$. Since, the sum of the internal angles of each triangle is 180 degrees. So, $0 < x < 90°$. Hence, $x = 30°$. Therefore, the measure of angle $\angle MNO$ is $\angle MNP + \angle PNO = 90° + x = 90° + 30° = 120°$ degrees.

50) Choice B is correct.

We know that: $sin^2\,a + cos^2\,a = 1$. Therefore:

$3x - 2\,sin^2\,a - 2\,cos^2\,a = 4 \rightarrow 3x - 2(sin^2\,a + cos^2\,a) = 4 \rightarrow 3x - 2 = 4 \rightarrow 3x = 4 + 2 = 6 \rightarrow x = 2$.

Trigonometry Practice Tests 2 Explanations

1) Choice D is correct.

The function is $f(x) = 2 - 3\sin\left(2x - \frac{\pi}{3}\right)$.

Determine the Domain:

The domain of a function is the set of all possible input values (often denoted as x −values) which will provide a valid output from a particular function. For the sine function (and all its transformations), the domain is all real numbers. This is because any real number can be inputted into the sine function and it will yield a real number output. The $\left(2x - \frac{\pi}{3}\right)$ part inside the sine function doesn't restrict the domain as it is a linear transformation that also allows all real numbers. So, the domain of this function is all real numbers, or in interval notation, $(-\infty, +\infty)$.

Determine the Range:

The range of a function is the set of all possible output values (often denoted as y −values) which are valid for a given input to the function. The sine function has a range of $[-1,1]$ on its own, but there are transformations applied to it in this function.

The $3\,sin\left(2x - \frac{\pi}{3}\right)$ part stretches the range to $[-3,3]$ because the amplitude (or peak value) of the sine wave is multiplied by 3:

$-1 \le sin\left(2x - \frac{\pi}{3}\right) \le 1 \rightarrow -3 \le 3\,sin\left(2x - \frac{\pi}{3}\right) \le 3$

As the same way, we get:

$-3 \le 3\,sin\left(2x - \frac{\pi}{3}\right) \le 3 \rightarrow -3 \le -3\,sin\left(2x - \frac{\pi}{3}\right) \le 3$

$\rightarrow 2 - 3 \le 2 - 3\,sin\left(2x - \frac{\pi}{3}\right) \le 2 + 3$

$\rightarrow -1 \le f(x) \le 5$

So, the range becomes $[-1,5]$. So, the domain is $(-\infty, +\infty)$ and the range is $[-1,5]$.

2) Choice D is correct.

Rewrite the given equation as follows. We know that $cos\left(x-\frac{\pi}{2}\right)=sin\,x$, so we have: $y=\frac{1}{sin\,x}+4$. Since $\frac{1}{sin\,x}=csc\,x$, we get: $y=csc\,x+4$. Now, you see that the equation is the cosecant function, translated 4 units upward. The cosecant function is the reciprocal of the sine function and has vertical asymptotes where the sine function is zero. That is, the vertical lines $x=n\pi$ are asymptotes, where n is an integer. Therefore, the correct answer is:

D. It represents a cosine function, $y=csc\,x$, translated 4 units upwards.

3) Choice C is correct.

We know that: $tan\,\theta=\frac{opposite}{adjacent}$, and $tan\,\theta=\frac{8}{15}$, therefore, the opposite side of the angle x is 8 and the adjacent side is 15. Let's draw the triangle. Using the Pythagorean theorem, we have:

$a^2+b^2=c^2\rightarrow 8^2+15^2=c^2\rightarrow 64+225=c^2\rightarrow c=17$,

$sin\,x=\frac{opposite}{hypotenuse}=\frac{8}{17}$.

4) Choice A is correct.

We know that $csc\,\theta$ is the reciprocal of $sin\,\theta$, i.e., $csc\,\theta=\frac{1}{sin\,\theta}$, and that $\cos(90°-\theta)=\sin(\theta)$. Hence, the expression becomes:

$$4\,cos\,70°\,csc\,20°+3\,cos\,60°\,csc\,30°=4\frac{cos\,70°}{sin\,20°}+3\frac{cos\,60°}{sin\,30°}$$

$$=4\frac{cos\,70°}{cos(90°-20°)}+3\frac{cos\,60°}{cos(90°-30°)}$$

$$=4\frac{cos\,70°}{cos\,70°}+3\frac{cos\,60°}{cos\,60°}$$

Since any number divided by itself is 1 (excluding zero), the expression simplifies to:

$4\,cos\,70°\,csc\,20°+3\,cos\,60°\,csc\,30°=4\times1+3\times1=4+3=7$

So, the answer is A, 7.

5) Choice D is correct.

Firstly, we can rule out options A and C as they are secant and tangent functions respectively, and our graph shows a cosine function. Between options B and D, we can see that option D matches our graph perfectly. It's a cosine function (matching the shape of our graph), it has an amplitude of 2 (the graph oscillates between -1 and 3, a range of 4, and half of this range gives an amplitude of 2), and it's been translated 1 unit down (the midline of the graph is at $y = -1$). Therefore, the correct answer is: D, $y = 2\,cos(x) - 1$.

6) Choice A is correct.

This can be written as $f(x) = sin(x)\,[sin^2(x) + 6\,sin(x) + 8]$. We can see that this function equals zero when $sin(x) = 0$. We know that $sin(x) = 0$ for $x = n\pi$ where n is an integer. So, the function equals zero at these points.

To find the other roots, we need to solve the quadratic equation $sin^2(x) + 6\,sin(x) + 8 = 0$. We can solve this using the quadratic formula: $x_{1,2} = \frac{-b\pm\sqrt{b^2-4ac}}{2a}$, for $ax^2 + bx + c = 0$. For our equation, $a = 1$, $b = 6$, $c = 8$. We find: $sin(x) = \frac{-6\pm\sqrt{6^2-4\times1\times8}}{2\times1} = \frac{-6\pm\sqrt{36-32}}{2} = \frac{-6\pm2}{2}$. So, $sin(x) = -4$ or $sin(x) = -2$.

However, these are not valid since the range of the sine function is $-1 \le sin(x) \le 1$. Therefore, the only roots of the function are $x = n\pi$ where n is an integer. This corresponds to answer option A: $\{0, \pi\}$.

7) Choice B is correct.

To find the inverse of $f(x) = 1 - sin(x)$, we first set $f(x)$ equal to y, resulting in $y = 1 - sin(x)$. Then we swap x and y to find the inverse: $x = 1 - sin(y)$. Solving this for y involves several steps:

1. We isolate the sin function: $sin(y) = 1 - x$.
2. Next, we need to reverse the sine operation by applying the $arcsin$ to both sides, remembering that $arcsin$ is the inverse function of sine: $y = arcsin(1 - x)$.

So, the correct answer is B, $f^{-1}(x) = arcsin(1 - x)$.

8) Choice A is correct.

We know that π radians $= 180°$, so $1° = \frac{\pi}{180}$ radians. Therefore, $15° = 15° \times \frac{\pi}{180°} = \frac{\pi}{12}$ radians. Hence, the correct option is A, $\frac{\pi}{12}$.

9) Choice B is correct.

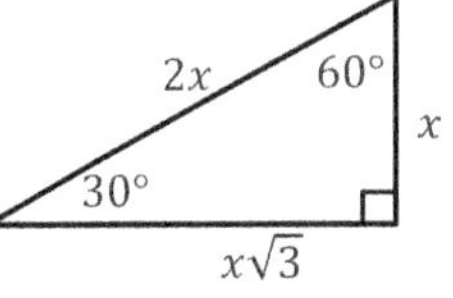

Consider the relationship among all sides of the special right triangle 30°-60°-90° is provided in this triangle:

In this triangle, the opposite side of the 30° angle is half of the hypotenuse. Draw the shape of this question: The ladder is the hypotenuse.

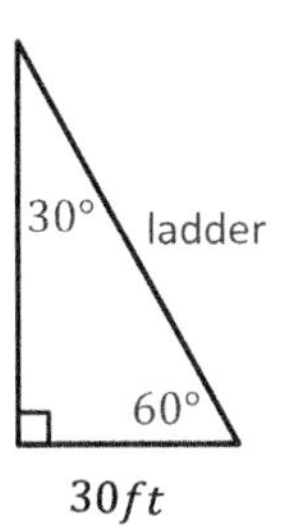

$\cos 60° = \frac{adjacent}{hypotenuse} \rightarrow \frac{1}{2} = \frac{30}{ladder} \rightarrow ladder = 60.$

Therefore, the ladder is $60ft$.

10) Choice D is correct.

The standard form of the tangent function is $f(x) = a\tan(b(x-c)) + d$, where:

b determines the period of the function (period $= \frac{\pi}{b}$ for tan).

c is the phase shift (how much the function is shifted horizontally).

d is the vertical shift (how much the function is shifted vertically).

a is the vertical stretch or compression factor (not required for this problem).

Given that:

The period is π, which suggests that $b = 1$ (since $\frac{\pi}{b} = \pi$).

The phase shift is 1 unit to the right, so $c = \frac{\pi}{2}$.

The vertical shift is 2 units up, so $d = 2$.

We consider function $y = \tan x$ and apply the above steps to reach the desired graph.

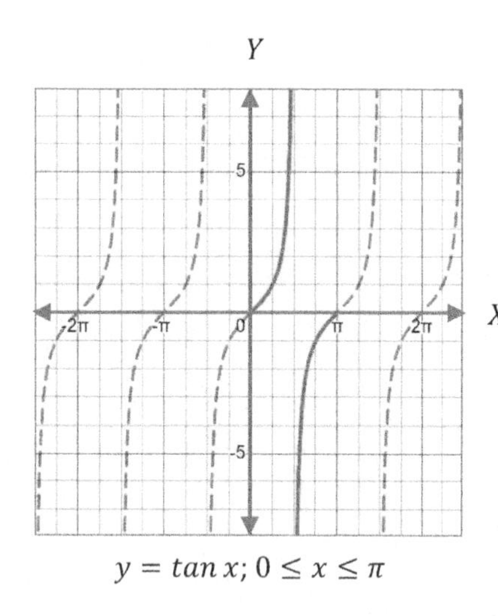

$y = tan\,x; 0 \leq x \leq \pi$

Shift $\frac{\pi}{2}$ unite to the right

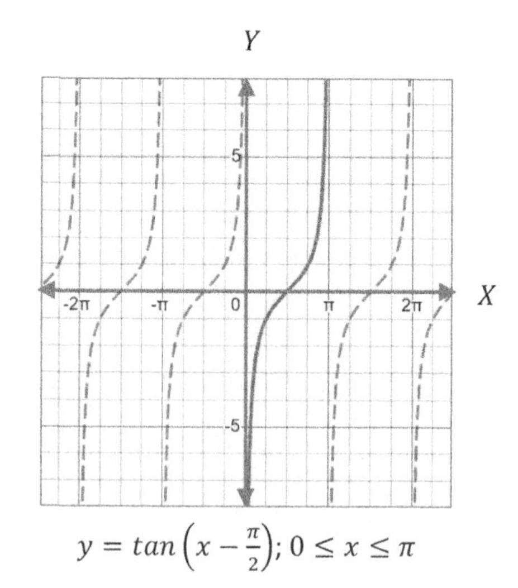

$y = tan\left(x - \frac{\pi}{2}\right); 0 \leq x \leq \pi$

Now, we shift the obtained graph up 2 units.

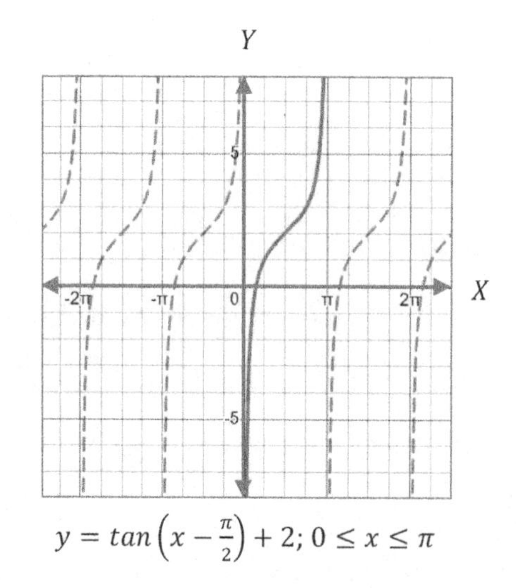

$y = tan\left(x - \frac{\pi}{2}\right) + 2; 0 \leq x \leq \pi$

The red part of the graph is the desired answer and corresponds to choice D.

11) Choice D is correct.

Given the quadrilateral $ABCD$ with diameter BD drawn, $\angle BAD = 60°$, $AB = 9\ cm$, and $\angle DBC = 45°$, the length of side DC can be found as follows:

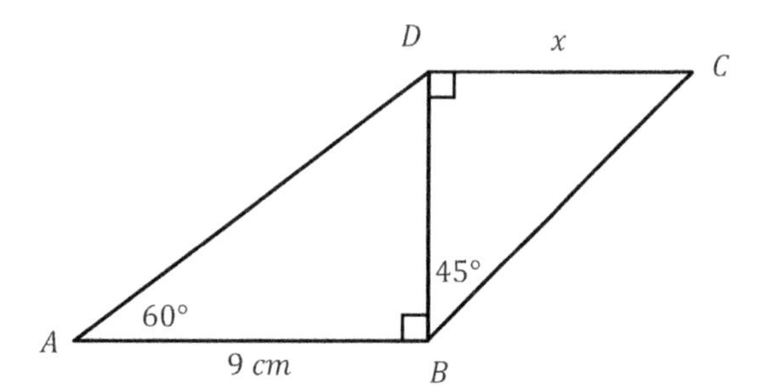

Firstly, note that because BD is the diameter, which is the common side of two right-angled triangles ABD with right angle at $\angle ABD$ and BDC with right angled at $\angle BDC$. By using the tangent of the angle BAD, find the length of the side BD. So, we get:

$$tan\ \angle BAD = \frac{BD}{AB} \rightarrow tan\ 60° = \frac{BD}{9} \rightarrow BD = 9\sqrt{3}$$

Now, to find $x = DC$, it is enough to evaluate the tangent of 45°. Hence,

$$tan\ \angle DBC = \frac{DC}{BD} \rightarrow tan\ 45° = \frac{x}{9\sqrt{3}} \rightarrow x = 9\sqrt{3}$$

Therefore, the length of side x is $9\sqrt{3}\ cm$.

12) Choice B is correct.

Let's denote the width of the river as "d".

From Z's point of view, we can form a right triangle ZXW where $\angle Z = 30°$. Here, the opposite side is "d" (the width of the river) and the adjacent side is the line connecting Z and W, which is given as $(120 - x)$ meters and x is the distance between Z and W.

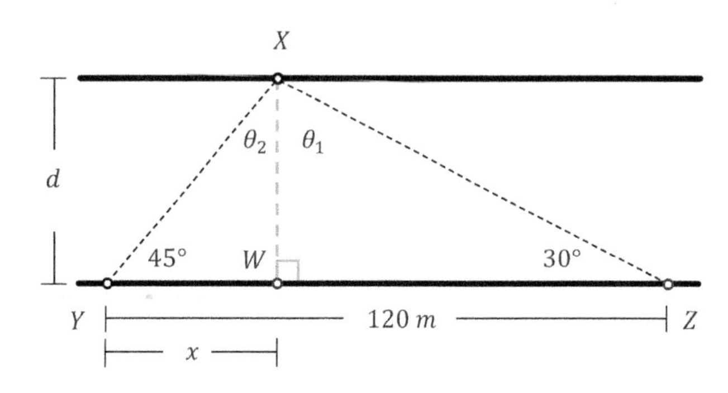

On the other hand, we know that the sum of the internal angles of each triangle is 180 degrees. Therefore, angles θ_1, θ_2, and X are respectively 60°, 45°, and 105°.

For ΔZXW: $90° + \theta_1 + 30° = 180° \rightarrow \theta_1 = 60°$

For ΔYXW: $90° + \theta_2 + 45° = 180° \rightarrow \theta_1 = 45°$

For ΔXZY: $45° + \angle X + 30° = 180° \rightarrow \angle X = 105°$

Since the tangent of $\angle\theta_1 = \frac{120-x}{d}$ and the tangent of $\angle\theta_2 = \frac{x}{d}$, we can solve for "$d$" as follows:

$$\theta_1 = 60° \rightarrow tan\,60° = \frac{120-x}{d} \rightarrow \sqrt{3} = \frac{120-x}{d} \rightarrow \sqrt{3}d + x = 120$$

$$\theta_1 = 45° \rightarrow tan\,45° = \frac{x}{d} \rightarrow 1 = \frac{x}{d} \rightarrow d = x$$

According to the second equation $d = x$, put d instead of x in the first equation.

$$d = x \rightarrow \sqrt{3}d + d = 120 \rightarrow (1 + \sqrt{3})d = 120 \rightarrow d = \frac{120}{1+\sqrt{3}}$$

So, the width of the river is $d = \frac{120}{1+\sqrt{3}}$ meters.

13) Choice C is correct.

To find the inverse of the function $f(x) = cos^2\left(\frac{1}{2}x - 1\right)$, we start by setting $f(x)$ equal to y: $y = cos^2\left(\frac{1}{2}x - 1\right)$. We swap x and y to find the inverse: $x = cos^2\left(\frac{1}{2}y - 1\right)$. Next, we take the square root of both sides:

$$x = cos^2\left(\frac{1}{2}y - 1\right) \rightarrow x = \left(cos\left(\frac{1}{2}y - 1\right)\right)^2$$

$$\rightarrow \sqrt{x} = cos\left(\frac{1}{2}y - 1\right)$$

Finally, we take the *arccos* of both sides: $\frac{1}{2}y - 1 = arccos(\sqrt{x})$. Now, isolate y:

$$\frac{1}{2}y - 1 = arccos(\sqrt{x}) \rightarrow \frac{1}{2}y = arccos(\sqrt{x}) + 1$$

$$y = 2\,arccos(\sqrt{x}) + 2$$

So, the correct answer is C, $f^{-1}(x) = 2\,arccos(\sqrt{x}) + 2$.

14) Choice A is correct.

$f(x) = cos\,x + 4$ will vary between 3 and 5. Because, $-1 \leq cos\,x \leq 1 \rightarrow 3 \leq cos\,x + 4 \leq 5$.

$g(x) = 2 - sin^2 x$ will vary between 1 and 2 since $sin^2 x$ will vary between 0 and 1. So, we get: $-1 \leq -sin^2 x \leq 0 \rightarrow 1 \leq 2 - sin^2 x \leq 2$.

The maximum value of $f(x)$ is 5, which is not the same as the maximum value of $g(x)$ equals to 2. Two functions spread along the $x-$axis between the maximum and minimum values. Since the interval of the range of function does not have a common point, it does not intersect at any point. Therefore, the correct answer is A.

15) Choice D is correct.

As $sin\,2\varphi = 2\,sin\,\varphi\,cos\,\varphi$, so $sin\,2\theta = 2\,sin\,\theta \times cos\,\theta = 2 \times 0.3 = 0.6$. Since $sin\,2\theta = 0.6$ and $sin^2\varphi + cos^2\varphi = 1$, then $(0.6)^2 + cos^2 2\theta = 1 \rightarrow cos\,2\theta = 0.8$. Now, as $cos\,2\varphi = 2\,cos^2\varphi - 1$, we have $0.8 = 2\,cos^2\theta - 1 \rightarrow cos^2\theta = 0.9$. Also, we get $sin^2\theta + 0.9 = 1$, so $sin^2\theta = 0.1$. Next, substituting this back into the expression $sin^2\theta - cos^2\theta$, we get:

$cos^2\theta - sin^2\theta = 0.9 - 0.1 = 0.8$. Hence, the correct option is D, 0.8.

16) Choice B is correct.

First, notice that the value of $cos\,\theta$ is between -1 and 1 for any angle θ. This means that $x^2 - x + 1$ must also be between -1 and 1. If we try the options given in the problem one by one, we can check which one gives us a value for $x^2 - x + 1$ in the range $[-1,1]$.

Option A. -1: $(-1)^2 - (-1) + 1 = 1 + 1 + 1 = 3$, which is not in the range $[-1,1]$.

Option B. 0: $0^2 - 0 + 1 = 1$, which is in the range $[-1,1]$.

Option C. 1: $1^2 - 1 + 1 = 1$, which is in the range $[-1,1]$.

It turns out that all the given options are possible solutions. However, we need to check if they actually satisfy the given equation. Checking these values, we find:

For $x = 0$; $cos\left(\frac{\pi(0)}{2}\right) = cos\,0 = 1$, which does equal $0^2 - 0 + 1 = 1$.

For $x = 1$; $cos\left(\frac{\pi(1)}{2}\right) = cos\left(\frac{\pi}{2}\right) = 0$, which does not equal $1^2 - 1 + 1 = 1$.

So, the only solution is B, 0.

17) Choice A is correct.

To find the right choice, we consider graph $y = sin\left(x - \frac{\pi}{3}\right)$. Figure below.

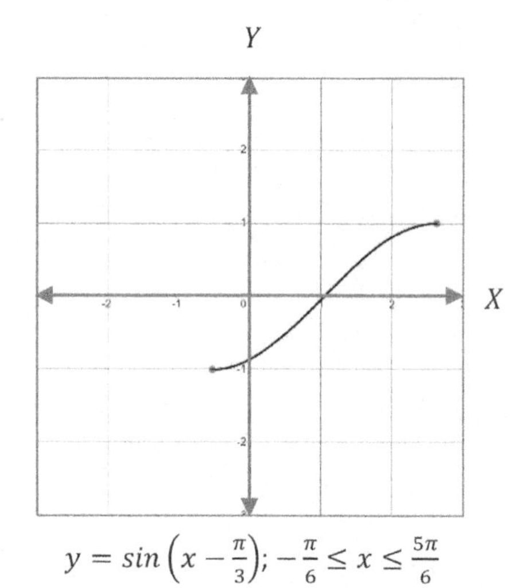

$y = sin\left(x - \frac{\pi}{3}\right); -\frac{\pi}{6} \leq x \leq \frac{5\pi}{6}$

Considering that in the given interval the function is one to one, then the inverse level of the function was determined.

In the next step, we determine the image of this graph relative to line $y = x$. figure below.

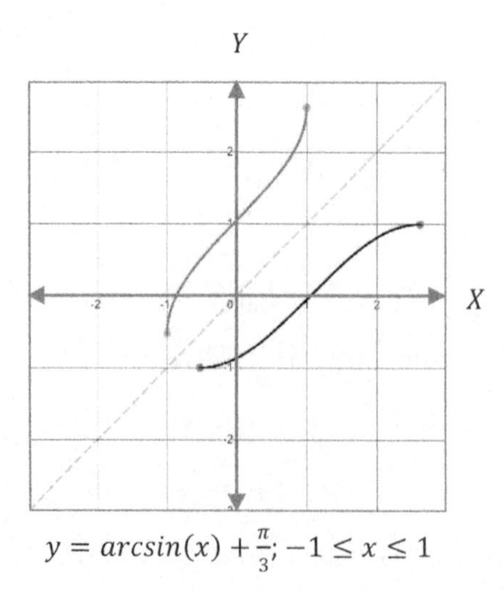

$y = arcsin(x) + \frac{\pi}{3}; -1 \leq x \leq 1$

As a choice A, answers are appropriate.

18) Choice A is correct.

In a right-angled triangle, we can use trigonometric ratios to find the value of $(\sec X + \tan X)$. From the given information, we know that $XZ - YZ = 1\,cm \rightarrow YZ = XZ - 1$, so we have: $\tan X = \frac{YZ}{XY}$ and $\sec X = \frac{XZ}{XY}$.

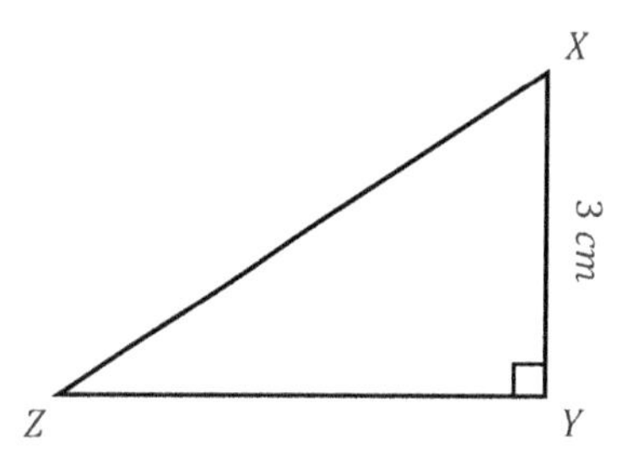

Now, we are given $XY = 3\,cm$. Using Pythagoras' theorem, we have:

$$XZ^2 = XY^2 + YZ^2 \rightarrow XZ^2 = 3^2 + (XZ - 1)^2$$

$$\rightarrow XZ^2 = 9 + XZ^2 - 2XZ + 1$$

$$\rightarrow 10 - 2XZ = 0$$

$$\rightarrow XZ = 5$$

So, the length of the side YZ is equal $4\,cm$. Substituting this back into the expression, we get: $(\sec X + \tan X) = \left(\frac{1}{\cos X} + \frac{\sin X}{\cos X}\right) = \frac{1+\sin X}{\cos X}$. Since we have $YZ = 4\,cm$, $XZ = 5\,cm$ and $XY = 3\,cm$, we know that $\sin X = \frac{YZ}{XZ} = \frac{4}{5}$ and $\cos X = \frac{XY}{XZ} = \frac{3}{5}$.

Therefore,

$$(\sec X + \tan X) = \frac{1+\frac{4}{5}}{\frac{3}{5}} = \frac{\frac{9}{5}}{\frac{3}{5}} = 3.$$

The correct answer is A, 3.

19) Choice A is correct.

Use this formula: $Degrees = Radian \times \frac{180}{\pi}$,

$$Degrees = \frac{2\pi}{3} \times \frac{180}{\pi} = \frac{360\pi}{3\pi} = 120$$

20) Choice D is correct.

Given $sin(A - B) = \frac{\sqrt{3}}{2}$ and $cos(A + B) = \frac{1}{2}$. From $sin(A - B) = \frac{\sqrt{3}}{2}$, we know that $A - B = \frac{\pi}{3}$ because $sin\left(\frac{\pi}{3}\right) = \frac{\sqrt{3}}{2}$. And from $cos(A + B) = \frac{1}{2}$, we know that $A + B = \frac{\pi}{3}$, because $cos\left(\frac{\pi}{3}\right) = \frac{1}{2}$. Since $A + B$ is an acute angle, we take $A + B = \frac{\pi}{3}$. Solving these two equations simultaneously, we get:

$$\begin{cases} A - B = \frac{\pi}{3} \\ A + B = \frac{\pi}{3} \end{cases}$$

Adding the equations, $2A = \frac{2\pi}{3}$, so $A = \frac{\pi}{3}$. Therefore, the correct answer is D, $\frac{\pi}{3}$.

21) Choice D is correct.

Use this formula: $Radian = Degrees \times \frac{\pi}{180}$.

$$Radian = 150 \times \frac{\pi}{180} = \frac{150\pi}{180} = \frac{5\pi}{6}$$

22) Choice D is correct.

In a right triangle ABC, where $\angle C = 90°$ and the sides BC and BA are given as 14 cm and 16 cm respectively, we can calculate angle BAC using the sine function. The sine of an angle in a right triangle is the ratio of the length of the side opposite the angle to the length of the hypotenuse. Therefore, $sin(BAC) = \frac{BC}{BA} = \frac{14}{16} = 0.875$.

To find angle BAC, we would take the inverse sine ($arcsin$ or sin^{-1}) of 0.875. Doing this calculation: $\angle BAC = sin^{-1}(0.875) \approx 61.04°$. So, $\angle BAC$ is approximately 60°.

23) Choice B is correct.

The general form of a sinusoidal function is given by $f(x) = a\,sin\big(b(x - c)\big) + d$ or $f(x) = a\,cos\big(b(x - c)\big) + d$, where:

1. a is the amplitude of the function.
2. b determines the period of the function (period $= \frac{2\pi}{b}$).
3. c is the phase shift (how much the function is shifted horizontally).

4. d is the vertical shift (how much the function is shifted vertically).

Given that:

5. Amplitude is 3 (so $a = 3$)
6. Period is π (so $b = 2$, since $\frac{2\pi}{b} = \pi$)
7. Phase shift is $\frac{\pi}{2}$ units to the right (so $c = \frac{\pi}{2}$)
8. Vertical shift is 1 unit down (so $d = -1$)

The function reaches its minimum at $x = 0$. Since the cosine function reaches its maximum at $x = 0$ and we are dealing with a minimum, we need a negative cosine function. Substituting all these values into the equation, we get: $f(x) = -3\cos\left(2\left(x + \frac{\pi}{2}\right)\right) - 1$.

So, the correct answer is option B: $f(x) = -3\cos\left(2\left(x + \frac{\pi}{2}\right)\right) - 1$.

24) Choice A is correct.

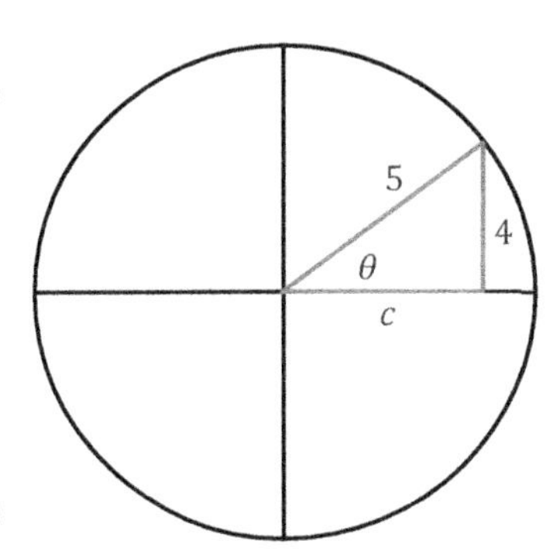

Since: $\sin\theta = \frac{opposite}{hypotenuse} = \frac{4}{5}$. Now, we have the following triangle. Then:

$c = \sqrt{5^2 - 4^2} = \sqrt{25 - 16} = \sqrt{9} = \pm 3$, so:

$\cos\theta = \frac{adjacent}{hypotenuse} = \frac{3}{5}$ or $\cos\theta = -\frac{3}{5}$.

We know that θ is an acute angle. Then, $\cos\theta$ is positive. Therefore, $\cos\theta = \frac{3}{5}$.

25) Choice A is correct.

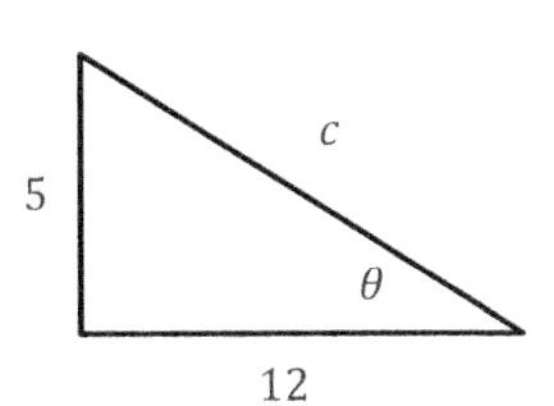

We know that: $\tan\theta = \frac{opposite}{adjacent}$, $\tan\theta = \frac{5}{12}$. So, we have the following right triangle. Then:

$c = \sqrt{5^2 + 12^2} = \sqrt{25 + 144} = \sqrt{169} = 13$,

$\cos\theta = \frac{adjacent}{hypotenuse} = \frac{12}{13}$.

26) Choice B is correct.

Given that triangle ABC is right-angled at C with hypotenuse $AB = 19\ cm$ and $\angle B = 22°$ degrees, you want to find the length of side BC. The length of side BC can be calculated using the cosine of $\angle B$ (which is the ratio of the adjacent side to the hypotenuse in a right-angled triangle). We know that $cos(B) = \frac{BC}{AB}$, so:

$BC = AB \times cos(B) \rightarrow BC = 19\ cm \times cos\ 22°$

$\rightarrow BC = 19\ cm \times 0.927$

$\rightarrow BC = 17.613\ cm$

Therefore, the length of side BC is approximately $17.6\ cm$.

27) Choice B is correct.

θ is an acute angle. Then, the trigonometric ratios for θ are positive. $sin\ A = \frac{1}{4}$. Since $sin\ \theta = \frac{opposite}{hypotenuse}$, we have the following right triangle. Then:

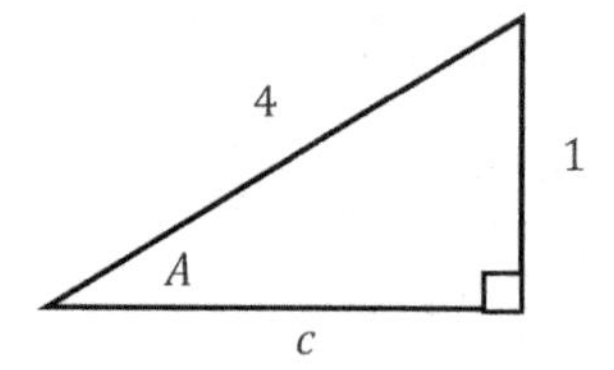

$c = \sqrt{4^2 - 1^2} = \sqrt{16 - 1} = \sqrt{15}$.

$cos\ A = \frac{adjacent}{hypotenuse} = \frac{\sqrt{15}}{4}$.

28) Choice C is correct.

To find the coterminal angle to angle $125°$:

$125° + 360° = 485°$

$125° - 360° = -235°$

29) Choice B is correct.

The cotangent is the reciprocal of the tangent as $cot\ x = \frac{1}{tan\ x}$, so when $cot\left(\frac{\pi}{2} - \frac{\varphi}{2}\right) = \sqrt{3}$, this is the same as saying that $tan\left(\frac{\pi}{2} - \frac{\varphi}{2}\right) = \frac{1}{\sqrt{3}}$.

$$cot\left(\frac{\pi}{2} - \frac{\varphi}{2}\right) = \sqrt{3} \rightarrow \frac{1}{tan\left(\frac{\pi}{2} - \frac{\varphi}{2}\right)} = \sqrt{3} \rightarrow tan\left(\frac{\pi}{2} - \frac{\varphi}{2}\right) = \frac{1}{\sqrt{3}}$$

This ratio of $\frac{1}{\sqrt{3}}$ or $\frac{\sqrt{3}}{3}$ corresponds to an angle of $\frac{\pi}{6}$ (or 30 degrees) in the unit circle.

So, we have:

$$tan\left(\frac{\pi}{2}-\frac{\varphi}{2}\right)=\frac{1}{\sqrt{3}} \rightarrow tan\left(\frac{\pi}{2}-\frac{\varphi}{2}\right)=tan\frac{\pi}{6} \rightarrow \frac{\pi}{2}-\frac{\varphi}{2}=\frac{\pi}{6} \rightarrow \varphi=\frac{2\pi}{3}$$

The sine of an angle of $\frac{2\pi}{3}$ (or 120 degrees) in the unit circle is $\frac{\sqrt{3}}{2}$. The choice B is correct answer.

30) Choice C is correct.

To find the value of $sin\,45°\,cos\,15°$, we can use the trigonometric identity: $sin(A)\,cos(B)=\frac{1}{2}[sin(A+B)+sin(A-B)]$. Applying this identity, we have:

$$sin\,45°\,cos\,15°=\frac{1}{2}[sin(45°+15°)+sin(45°-15°)]$$

$$=\frac{1}{2}[sin\,60°+sin\,30°]$$

$$=\frac{1}{2}\left[\frac{\sqrt{3}}{2}+\frac{1}{2}\right]=\frac{\sqrt{3}+1}{4}$$

Therefore, the value of $4(sin\,45°\,cos\,15°)$ is $4\left(\frac{\sqrt{3}+1}{4}\right)=\sqrt{3}+1$.

31) Choice B is correct.

For a right-angled triangle with $\angle A=90°$, $sin^2 A=sin^2 90°=1$. As B and C are acute angles then $sin\,C=sin(90°-B)=cos\,B$ and $sin^2 B+cos^2 B=1$. Hence the sum $sin^2 A+sin^2 B+sin^2 C=1+1=2$. Hence, the correct option is B, 2.

32) Choice D is correct.

To find the value of $\frac{sin\,\theta+cos\,\theta}{sin\,\theta-cos\,\theta}$ based on the given value of $tan\,\theta$, we can use trigonometric identities to manipulate the expression. Given that $tan\,\theta=\frac{3}{4}$, we can represent this as $\frac{sin\,\theta}{cos\,\theta}=\frac{3}{4}$. We can rearrange this equation to isolate $sin\,\theta$ and $cos\,\theta$: $sin\,\theta=\frac{3}{4}cos\,\theta$.

Now, let's substitute this expression into the given expression:

$$\frac{sin\,\theta+cos\,\theta}{sin\,\theta-cos\,\theta}=\frac{\frac{3}{4}cos\,\theta+cos\,\theta}{\frac{3}{4}cos\,\theta-cos\,\theta}=\frac{\frac{7}{4}cos\,\theta}{-\frac{1}{4}cos\,\theta}=-7$$

Therefore, the value of $\frac{sin\,\theta+cos\,\theta}{sin\,\theta-cos\,\theta}$ is: D. -7.

33) Choice A is correct.

To find the value of $m^2 + n^2$ based on the given expressions for m and n, we can substitute the values and simplify. Let's calculate $m^2 + n^2$:

$$m^2 + n^2 = (3\cos x - \sin x)^2 + (\cos x + 3\sin x)^2$$

$$= 9\cos^2 x - 6\cos x \sin x + \sin^2 x + \cos^2 x + 6\cos x \sin x + 9\sin^2 x$$

$$= 9\cos^2 x + \sin^2 x + \cos^2 x + 9\sin^2 x$$

$$= 10\cos^2 x + 10\sin^2 x$$

$$= 10(\cos^2 x + \sin^2 x)$$

$$= 10$$

Therefore, $m^2 + n^2$ is equal to: A. 10.

34) Choice D is correct.

The equation $\cos\alpha \csc 19° = 1$ can be written as $\cos\alpha = \sin 19°$, because $\csc 19°$ is the reciprocal of $\sin 19°$. That is, $\csc 19° = \frac{1}{\sin 19°}$. Therefore,

$$\cos\alpha \csc 19° = 1 \rightarrow \cos\alpha \frac{1}{\sin 19°} = 1 \rightarrow \cos\alpha = \sin 19°$$

Since $\cos\alpha = \sin(90° - \alpha)$, we get:

$$\cos\alpha = \sin 19° \rightarrow \sin(90° - \alpha) = \sin 19° \rightarrow 90° - \alpha = 19° \rightarrow \alpha = 71°$$

Hence, the correct answer is 71° (Option D).

35) Choice A is correct.

The formula for $\cos C + \cos D$ is $2\cos\left[\frac{C+D}{2}\right]\cos\left[\frac{C-D}{2}\right]$. Hence, the correct option is A, $x = 2\cos\left[\frac{C+D}{2}\right]\cos\left[\frac{C-D}{2}\right]$.

36) Choice D is correct.

To solve this problem, use $\sin^2 A + \cos^2 A = 1 \rightarrow \cos^2 A = 1 - \sin^2 A$. We get:

$$\frac{\cos^2 A}{1+\sin A} = \frac{1-\sin^2 A}{1+\sin A} = \frac{(1+\sin A)(1-\sin A)}{1+\sin A} = 1 - \sin A$$

Next, for the other part of the expression, we take the common denominator and simplify.

$$\frac{1+\sin A}{\cos A} - \frac{\cos A}{1-\sin A} = \frac{(1+\sin A)(1-\sin A) - \cos^2 A}{\cos A(1-\sin A)}$$

$$= \frac{1 - sin^2 A - cos^2 A}{cos A(1 - sin A)}$$

$$= \frac{1 - (sin^2 A + cos^2 A)}{cos A(1 - sin A)}$$

$$= \frac{1 - 1}{cos A(1 - sin A)} = 0$$

Now, substitute the obtained terms:

$$1 - \left[\frac{cos^2 A}{1 + sin A}\right] + \left[\frac{1 + sin A}{cos A} - \frac{cos A}{1 - sin A}\right] = 1 - (1 - sin A) + 0 = sin A$$

37) Choice C is correct.

The sum of the angles in a triangle is $180°$. So, if the ratio of the angles is $3:8:9$, then the angles are $3x$, $8x$, and $9x$. Since these angles add up to $180°$, we have the equation $3x + 8x + 9x = 180°$. Solving for x gives $20x = 180° \rightarrow x = 9°$. Substituting x back into $3x$, $8x$, and $9x$, we find the angles are $27°$, $72°$, and $81°$ respectively. Therefore, the correct answer is $27°$, $72°$, $81°$ (Option C).

38) Choice C is correct.

We have $\angle DAC + \angle ACD + \angle CDA = 180°$, for the triangle ACD. On the other hand, we know that the interior angles of the rectangle are 90 degrees. So, we get:

$$\angle DAC + \angle ACD + \angle CDA = 180° \rightarrow \angle DAC + \angle ACD = 90°$$

$$\rightarrow \angle DAC = 90° - \angle ACD$$

In addition, $\angle ACD = \angle BAC$.

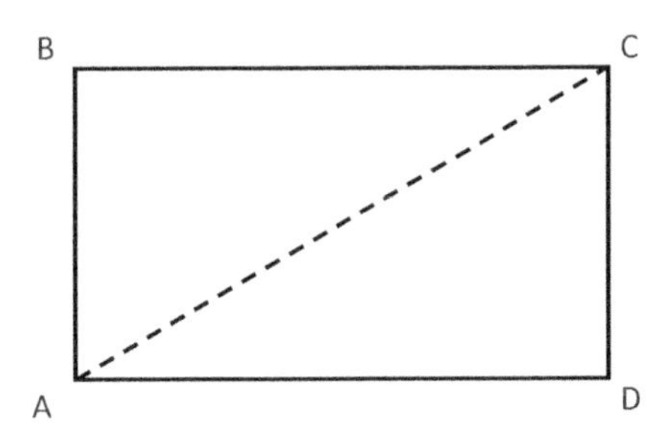

Let's denote $\angle ACD$ and $\angle BAC$ as θ. The given expression can be simplified as:

$$(tan^2 \theta + 1) sin^2(90° - \theta)$$

We know that $tan^2 \theta + 1 = sec^2 \theta$. Therefore, the expression simplifies to:

$$sec^2 \theta \, sin^2(90° - \theta)$$

Using $sin(90° - \theta) = cos\,\theta$, we can further simplify: $sec^2\,\theta\,cos^2\,\theta$. Since $sec\,\theta = \frac{1}{cos\,\theta}$, and $sec\,\theta \cdot cos\,\theta = 1$. We get: $sec^2\,\theta\,cos^2\,\theta = (sec\,\theta \cdot cos\,\theta)^2 = 1$.

The value of $(tan^2\,\angle ACD + 1)\,sin^2\,\angle DAC$ is 1, so the correct answer is C, 1.

39) Choice D is correct.

The cotangent is the reciprocal of tangent: $tan\,\beta = \frac{1}{cot\,\beta} = \frac{1}{1} = 1$.

40) Choice D is correct.

Let's denote the height of the lighthouse as "h". The height h can be determined by observing that the two right-angled triangles formed by the lighthouse and the two boats.

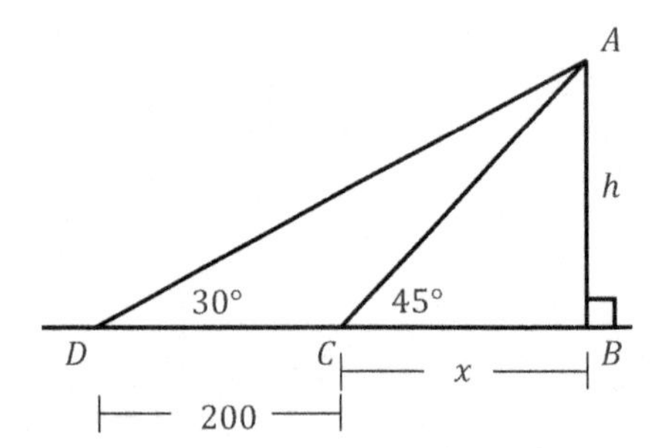

Find the tangent of the angles of the two boats. Let x be the distance of the closest boat to the lighthouse. Therefore, $tan\,45° = \frac{h}{x} \to h = x \times tan\,45° \to h = x$, and $tan\,30° = \frac{h}{200+x} \to h = (200 + x)\,tan\,30° \to \frac{\sqrt{3}}{3} \times (200 + x) = h \to 200\sqrt{3} + \sqrt{3}x = 3h$. Now, substitute h instead of x into the second equation, we get:

$200\sqrt{3} + \sqrt{3}h = 3h \to h = \frac{200\sqrt{3}}{3-\sqrt{3}} \to h = 100(1 + \sqrt{3})$.

Hence, the correct option is (D $100(1 + \sqrt{3})$ meter.

41) Choice C is correct.

We can rewrite the given equation using the double angle identity for cosine:

$2(sin^2\,\theta - cos^2\,\theta) = -1 \to 2((1 - cos^2\,\theta) - cos^2\,\theta) = -1$

$\to 2(1 - 2\,cos^2\,\theta) = -1$

Simplify:

$2(1 - 2\,cos^2\,\theta) = -1 \to 2 - 4\,cos^2\,\theta = -1 \to -4\,cos^2\,\theta = -3 \to cos^2\,\theta = \frac{3}{4}$.

Therefore, $\cos\theta = \frac{\sqrt{3}}{2}$ or $\cos\theta = -\frac{\sqrt{3}}{2}$. Since θ is a positive acute angle, then the value of $\cos\theta$ is $\frac{\sqrt{3}}{2}$. Hence, the correct answer is C, $\theta = 30°$. Because $\cos 30° = \frac{\sqrt{3}}{2}$.

42) Choice A is correct.

To simplify the expression, we can find $(\tan\theta - \sec\theta + 1)$ in the expression numerator as:

$$\frac{\tan\theta+\sec\theta-1}{\tan\theta-\sec\theta+1} = \frac{\tan\theta+\sec\theta-(\sec^2\theta-\tan^2\theta)}{\tan\theta-\sec\theta+1} = \frac{\tan\theta+\sec\theta-(\sec\theta+\tan\theta)(\sec\theta-\tan\theta)}{\tan\theta-\sec\theta+1}$$

$$= \frac{\tan\theta+\sec\theta-(\sec\theta+\tan\theta)(\sec\theta-\tan\theta)}{\tan\theta-\sec\theta+1} = \frac{(\tan\theta+\sec\theta)(1-\sec\theta+\tan\theta)}{\tan\theta-\sec\theta+1}$$

$$= \tan\theta + \sec\theta$$

Now, we can rewrite $\tan\theta$ as $\frac{\sin\theta}{\cos\theta}$ and $\sec\theta$ as $\frac{1}{\cos\theta}$. Substituting these values, we get:

$$\tan\theta + \sec\theta = \frac{\sin\theta}{\cos\theta} + \frac{1}{\cos\theta} = \frac{\sin\theta + 1}{\cos\theta}$$

Therefore, the correct answer is A, $\frac{\sin\theta+1}{\cos\theta}$.

43) Choice C is correct.

Let $2\cos\theta + 5\sin\theta = x$. To solve this problem, consider the following equations.

$$2\sin\theta - 5\cos\theta = 4$$
$$2\cos\theta + 5\sin\theta = x$$

Squaring both the equations and adding,

$$\begin{matrix} 2\sin\theta - 5\cos\theta = 4 \\ 2\cos\theta + 5\sin\theta = x \end{matrix} \rightarrow \begin{matrix} 4\sin^2\theta - 20\sin\theta\cos\theta + 25\cos^2\theta = 16 \\ 4\cos^2\theta + 20\sin\theta\cos\theta + 25\sin^2\theta = x^2 \end{matrix}$$

$$\rightarrow 29\sin^2\theta + 29\cos^2\theta = x^2 + 16$$

Simplify: $29(\sin^2\theta + \cos^2\theta) = x^2 + 16$. Since $\sin^2\theta + \cos^2\theta = 1$, then $x^2 + 16 = 29$. Therefore, $x^2 = 29 - 16 \rightarrow x^2 = 13 \rightarrow x = \pm\sqrt{13}$.

Hence, the choice C is correct.

44) Choice A is correct.

First, apply the squares:

$(\csc x \csc y + \cot x \cot y)^2 - (\csc x \cot y + \cot x \csc y)^2$

$= csc^2 x \, csc^2 y + 2 \, csc \, x \, csc \, y \, cot \, x \, cot \, y + cot^2 x \, cot^2 y - (csc^2 x \, cot^2 y +$
$2 \, csc \, x \, csc \, y \, cot \, x \, cot \, y + cot^2 x \, csc^2 y) = csc^2 x \, csc^2 y +$
$2 \, csc \, x \, csc \, y \, cot \, x \, cot \, y + cot^2 x \, cot^2 y - csc^2 x \, cot^2 y - 2 \, csc \, x \, cot \, y \, cot \, x \, csc \, y -$
$cot^2 x \, csc^2 y$

Next, simply:

$(csc \, x \, csc \, y + cot \, x \, cot \, y)^2 - (csc \, x \, cot \, y + cot \, x \, csc \, y)^2$
$= csc^2 x \, csc^2 y + cot^2 x \, cot^2 y - csc^2 x \, cot^2 y - cot^2 x \, csc^2 y$

Arrange the obtain expression, then factor:

$(csc \, x \, csc \, y + cot \, x \, cot \, y)^2 - (csc \, x \, cot \, y + cot \, x \, csc \, y)^2$
$= (csc^2 x \, csc^2 y - csc^2 x \, cot^2 y) + (cot^2 x \, cot^2 y - cot^2 x \, csc^2 y)$
$= csc^2 x \, (csc^2 y - cot^2 y) + cot^2 x \, (cot^2 y - csc^2 y)$
$= (csc^2 y - cot^2 y)(csc^2 x - cot^2 x)$

Since $csc^2 \theta = 1 + cot^2 \theta$ and $csc^2 \theta - cot^2 \theta = 1$, we get:

$(csc \, x \, csc \, y + cot \, x \, cot \, y)^2 - (csc \, x \, cot \, y + cot \, x \, csc \, y)^2 = (1)(1) = 1$

Therefore, the correct answer is A, 1.

45) Choice C is correct.

Since $sec \, \theta = \frac{1}{cos \, \theta}$, we have: $sec \, \theta + cos \, \theta = 2 \rightarrow \frac{1}{cos \, \theta} + cos \, \theta = 2$. Multiply both sides of the equation by $cos \, \theta$. So, $1 + cos^2 \theta = 2 \, cos \, \theta$. Now, rewrite the equation as: $cos^2 \theta - 2 \, cos \, \theta + 1 = 0$. Therefore, we get: $(cos \, \theta - 1)^2 = 0$, and $cos \, \theta - 1 = 0 \rightarrow cos \, \theta = 1$. Next, evaluate the value of $sec \, \theta$: $sec \, \theta = \frac{1}{cos \, \theta} \rightarrow sec \, \theta = 1$.

Finally, substitute the obtained value into the expression $sin^3 \theta + cos^3 \theta$ and calculate it.

$$sin^3 \theta + cos^3 \theta = (0)^3 + (1)^3 = 0 + 1 = 1$$

Therefore, the correct answer is C, 1.

46) Choice C is correct.

Let $\frac{sin \, \theta}{A} = \frac{cos \, \theta}{B} = \frac{1}{C}$. We have $C \, sin \, \theta = A$ and $C \, cos \, \theta = B$. Now, evaluate the value of

$$A^2 + B^2 = C^2 \sin^2\theta + C^2 \cos^2\theta = C^2(\sin^2\theta + \cos^2\theta) = C^2 \rightarrow C = \sqrt{A^2 + B^2}$$

Next, substitute $\frac{\sin\theta}{A} = \frac{1}{C} \rightarrow \sin\theta = \frac{A}{C}$ and $\cos\theta = \frac{B}{C}$ into the expression $\sin\theta + \cos\theta$ and calculate it:

$$\sin\theta + \cos\theta = \frac{A}{C} + \frac{B}{C} = \frac{A+B}{C} = \frac{A+B}{\sqrt{A^2+B^2}}$$

Choice C is correct.

47) Choice D is correct.

From the trigonometric identity $\csc^2\theta - \cot^2\theta = 1$, it follows that $\csc\theta = \pm\sqrt{\cot^2\theta + 1}$.

We're given that $\csc\theta - \cot\theta = \frac{5}{2}$, which we can rewrite as $\cot\theta = \csc\theta - \frac{5}{2}$. Substitute this into the derived expression for $\csc\theta$ to obtain:

$$\csc\theta = \pm\sqrt{\left(\csc\theta - \frac{5}{2}\right)^2 + 1}$$

To simplify the calculations, let's assume that $\csc\theta = x$. So, we have the equation:

$$x = \pm\sqrt{\left(x - \frac{5}{2}\right)^2 + 1}$$

Let's solve for x when the sign in front of the square root is positive. We obtain:

$$x = \sqrt{\left(x - \frac{5}{2}\right)^2 + 1}$$

Simplifying, we get: $\left(x - \frac{5}{2}\right)^2 + 1 = x^2$. Squaring both sides, we have: $\left(x^2 - 5x + \frac{25}{4}\right) + 1 = x^2$. Solving this quadratic equation gives two solutions: $-5x + \frac{25}{4} + 1 = 0 \rightarrow x = \frac{29}{20}$.

Note that the function $\csc$ is always greater than or equal to 1 in absolute value, so the solution must be $x = \frac{29}{20}$.

48) Choice D is correct.

In a right triangle SRT, where $\angle T = 90°$, $ST = 20\ cm$, and $\angle R = 55°$, you're asked to find the length of side RT. This task can be done using the sine rule, but it should be noted that the sine rule is typically used for non-right triangles. In the case of right triangles, it's simpler to use the direct relationship of the sine of an angle to the ratio of the length of the opposite side to the hypotenuse.

In any case, the sine rule states that the ratio of a side length to the sine of its opposite angle is the same for all sides in a triangle. Thus, for triangle SRT, we can write:

$$\frac{RT}{sin(\angle S)} = \frac{ST}{sin(\angle R)}$$

We know that $\angle S = 180° - 90° - 55° = 35°$ (since the sum of angles in a triangle is $180°$), $ST = 20\ cm$, and $\angle R = 55°$. Rearranging the equation to solve for RT gives:

$$RT = ST \times \frac{sin(\angle S)}{sin(\angle R)} = 20\ cm \times \frac{sin(35°)}{sin(55°)}$$

Therefore, plugging in the values and doing the calculations: $RT \approx 20\ cm \times \frac{0.5736}{0.8192} \approx 14\ cm$. So, the length of side RT is approximately $14\ cm$.

49) Choice B is correct.

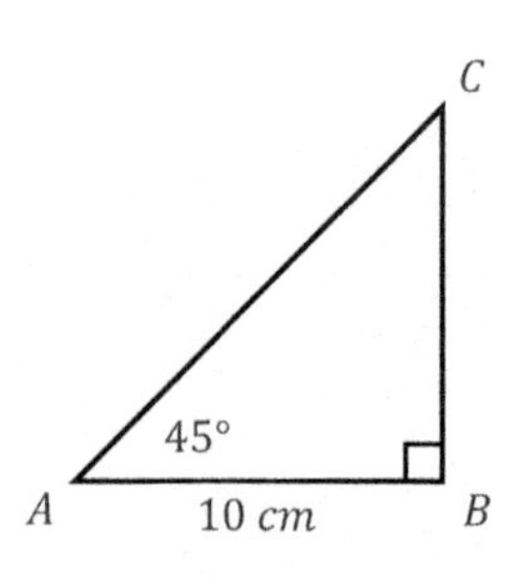

In a right-angled triangle ABC with $\angle B = 90°$ and $\angle A = 45°$, the ratio of the opposite side of the angle A to the hypotenuse of the triangle is $\frac{BC}{CA}$, which is equivalent to sine of the angle A (The same requested item in case of question). For $\angle A = 45°$, we have $sin\,45° = \frac{1}{\sqrt{2}}$. So, we get: $sin\,\angle A = \frac{BC}{CA} \rightarrow \frac{BC}{CA} = \frac{1}{\sqrt{2}}$. The correct answer is B.

50) Choice C is correct.

We know that $\cot\theta = \frac{1}{\tan\theta}$. So, we have:

$$\frac{\tan\theta}{1+\cot\theta} - \frac{\cot\theta}{1+\tan\theta} = \frac{\tan\theta}{1+\frac{1}{\tan\theta}} - \frac{\frac{1}{\tan\theta}}{1+\tan\theta} = \frac{\tan\theta}{\frac{\tan\theta+1}{\tan\theta}} - \frac{\frac{1}{\tan\theta}}{1+\tan\theta}$$

$$= \frac{\tan^2\theta}{\tan\theta+1} - \frac{1}{\tan\theta(1+\tan\theta)} = \frac{\tan^3\theta+1}{\tan\theta(\tan\theta+1)}$$

$$= \frac{(\tan\theta+1)^3-3\tan\theta(\tan\theta+1)}{\tan\theta(\tan\theta+1)} = \frac{(\tan\theta+1)[(\tan\theta+1)^2-3\tan\theta]}{\tan\theta(\tan\theta+1)}$$

$$= \frac{(\tan\theta+1)^2-3\tan\theta}{\tan\theta} = \frac{\tan^2\theta-\tan\theta+1}{\tan\theta} = \tan\theta + \frac{1}{\tan\theta} - 1$$

$$= \tan\theta + \cot\theta - 1$$

Therefore, the correct answer is C, $\tan\theta + \cot\theta - 1$.

Effortless Math's Trigonometry Online Center

... So Much More Online!

Effortless Math Online Trigonometry Center offers a complete study program, including the following:

- ✓ Step-by-step instructions on how to prepare for the Trigonometry test
- ✓ Numerous Trigonometry worksheets to help you measure your math skills
- ✓ Complete list of Trigonometry formulas
- ✓ Video lessons for Trigonometry topics
- ✓ Full-length Trigonometry practice tests
- ✓ And much more...

No Registration Required.

Visit **EffortlessMath.com/Trigonometry** to find your online Trigonometry resources.

Our Most Popular Books!

Pre-Algebra
Practice
Workbook

The Most Comprehensive
Review of Pre-Algebra 2024

2 full-length Pre-Algebra practice tests
Students #1 Choice

Comprehensive Pre-Algebra Practice WorkBook

Recommended by Teachers & Students

Reza Nazari

Download at

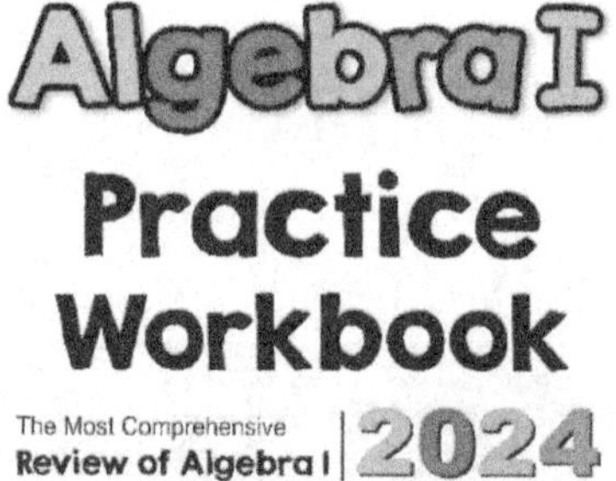

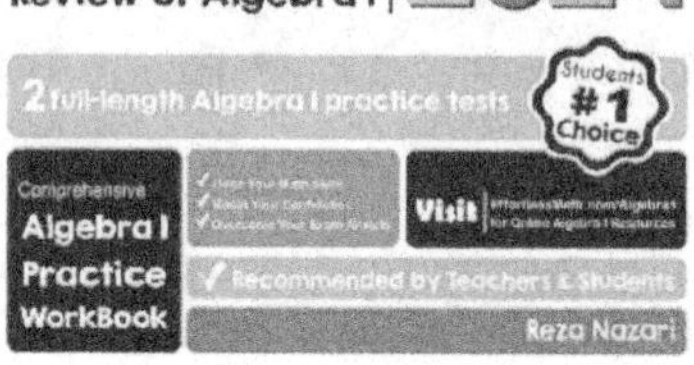

Download at

Algebra II
Practice
Workbook

The Most Comprehensive
Review of Algebra II 2024

2 full-length Algebra II practice tests
Students #1 Choice

Comprehensive Algebra II Practice WorkBook

Recommended by Teachers & Students

Reza Nazari

Download at

Download

Trigonometry
Practice
Workbook

The Most Comprehensive
Review for Trigonometry 2024

2 full-length Trigonometry practice tests
Test Taker's #1 Choice

Comprehensive Trigonometry Practice WorkBook

Recommended by Teachers & Students

Reza Nazari

Download at

Receive the PDF version of this book or get another FREE book!

Thank you for using our Book!

Do you LOVE this book?

Then, you can get the PDF version of this book or another book absolutely FREE!

Please email us at:

info@EffortlessMath.com

for details.

Author's Final Note

I hope you enjoyed reading this book. You've made it through the book! Great job!

First of all, thank you for purchasing this study guide. I know you could have picked any number of books to help you prepare for your Trigonometry course, but you picked this book and for that I am extremely grateful.

It took me years to write this study guide for the Trigonometry because I wanted to prepare a comprehensive Trigonometry study guide to help students make the most effective use of their valuable time while preparing for the final test.

After teaching and tutoring math courses for over a decade, I've gathered my personal notes and lessons to develop this study guide. It is my greatest hope that the lessons in this book could help you prepare for your test successfully.

If you have any questions, please contact me at reza@effortlessmath.com and I will be glad to assist. Your feedback will help me to greatly improve the quality of my books in the future and make this book even better. Furthermore, I expect that I have made a few minor errors somewhere in this study guide. If you think this to be the case, please let me know so I can fix the issue as soon as possible.

If you enjoyed this book and found some benefit in reading this, I'd like to hear from you and hope that you could take a quick minute to post a review on the book's Amazon page.

I personally go over every single review, to make sure my books really are reaching out and helping students and test takers. Please help me help Trigonometry students, by leaving a review!

I wish you all the best in your future success!

Reza Nazari

Math teacher and author

Printed in Great Britain
by Amazon